HOUGHTON MIFFLIN

WE·THE
PEOPLE

**Share
Our World**

Workbook for Reading and Review

Grade 3

Houghton Mifflin Company • Boston

Atlanta • Dallas • Denver • Geneva, Illinois • Palo Alto • Princeton

Share Our World

Designed by PiperStudiosInc.
Illustration: PiperStudiosInc.
Photography: © 1996 PhotoDisc, Inc.

Printed in the U.S.A.
ISBN: 0-618-01019-X

10-HS-05 04 03

Table of Contents

Share Our World

Table of Contents

WE·THE PEOPLE

Share Our World

Study Skills for Social Studies

Everyone studies. Studying is the way people learn new ideas. Studying means learning. Learning is different from memorizing. Learning involves your whole attention. It means organizing information in ways that help tie ideas together. It means making sense of new ideas and thinking them over. Learning happens most easily when you have a confident attitude and take an interest in your work.

(How to do it) **Here are some tips for studying:**

- **Give your whole attention to your study.** Find a quiet spot to work. Bring all of your study aids: notes, books, a pencil, some paper. Sit upright in a chair at a desk or table. Turn off the television. Let yourself concentrate.

- **Organize what you need to learn.** Think about your subject. What do you know and understand already? What do you still need to learn? If you can bring together what you already know with what you still need to know, your study will go smoothly. Try organizing like this:

Make a list of important ideas, key people, terms, and events.

Make a diagram of key concepts in the chapter.

Make a timeline showing important people and events.

Make a map showing important information.

Take notes about the things you think are important.

Highlight information that you need to know, so you can find it again easily.

- **Make sense of what you know.** Now think about the information you have organized. Does it make sense to you? Ask yourself questions to test your understanding. This is different from memorizing. Make sure you are thinking deeply. Do you know why an event is important? Do you understand how a key person influenced an event? Do you understand the ideas behind the events? Do you understand the ideas that influenced people to act? Keep reading and studying until your questions are answered.

  Why did Thomas Jefferson write the Declaration of Independence?

- **Rehearse what you know.** Now that you understand the subject, you'll need to remember it. This takes practice. It means going over what you know. You might reread your notes or book. You might memorize some information from a diagram or timeline. (See Tips for Remembering on pages 3 and 4.)

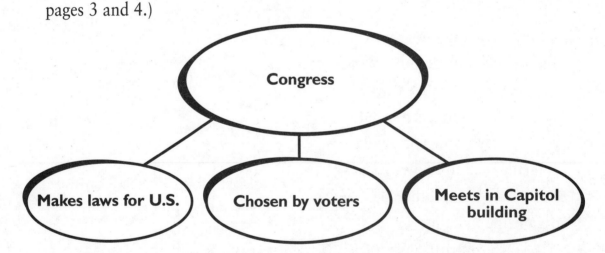

- **Be interested in your studies.** The subjects you are learning link you to human beings from the beginning of time. People everywhere think about the things you are being asked to learn. If you relate what you learn to yourself and to others, you'll find your studies take on new interest, even fun!

Tips for Remembering

Now that you've studied, how do you remember what you've learned? *Understanding* what you study is the best way to remember. But you will also need to *memorize*. Here are some tips to help you memorize.

How to do it To memorize an idea, a fact, a date, or a name, you need to repeat the information to yourself until it sticks in your head. Repeat. Repeat. Repeat. Here are several ways to do this:

> **Read the information.** Then look away and try to repeat it. Read the information again. Then look away and try to write it.
>
> **Listen to the information.** Have a friend read the information to you while you listen carefully. Or record the information on a cassette tape yourself and listen to it.
>
> **Practice repeating.** Go over the information more than once. Make flashcards with a question on the front of the card and the answer on the back. Practice at the breakfast table. Practice on the way to school.
>
> **Check yourself.** Ask a friend or relative to test you. You need to be sure you truly remember what you've been working on!
>
> **Overlearn.** To remember information for a long time, review many times. Review on different days. Practice until it's easy to recall.

More things you can do To memorize an idea, a fact, a date, or a name, you need to repeat the information to yourself until it sticks in your head. Repeat. Repeat. Repeat. Here are several ways to do this:

Rhymes Try creating a rhyme to help you remember very specific information. For example, students over the years have learned the dates that Columbus sailed to the Americas by remembering this rhyme:

> Fourteen hundred and ninety-two,
> Columbus sailed the ocean blue.
> Fourteen hundred and ninety-three,
> Columbus sailed the bright blue sea!

Memory Devices You can also make up special memory devices to help you remember. If you need to remember a series of things, make up a word or sentence to help. Here are two examples:

- You can remember all of the lakes in the Great Lakes by using the word HOMES. Each letter stands for one of the lakes: Huron, Ontario, Michigan, Erie, and Superior.

- Create a silly sentence to remember information in sequence. For example, students sometimes need to recall the order of the planets. Make a sentence in which each word starts with the letter of the name of a planet. Try something like, "My very eager mother just saw us near Paris." This stands for Mercury, Venus, Earth, Mars, Jupiter, Saturn, Uranus, Neptune, Pluto. It gives the planets in order starting with the closest to the sun.

Name _____ Date _____

Comprehension Strategy: Previewing a Lesson

People Live and Work in Communities

When you **preview** a lesson, you look ahead at it. You try
to get an idea of what it will be about.

Preview Lesson 1. Read the main headings. The headings are words in large red type. List the headings below. Also read the Main Idea sentence and the Focus questions below the headings.

1. p. 13 _____

2. p. 14 _____

3. p. 16 _____

Now describe the photographs in Lesson 1.

4. p. 13 _____

5. p. 14 _____

6. p. 15 _____

7. p. 17 _____

Think about the headings and the photographs. Then predict what you think you will learn from this lesson.

8. _____

_____

Read the lesson. Did you learn what you predicted you would learn? Explain.

9. _____

_____

Name _____ Date _____

People Live and Work in Communities

Review pages 13–17 to answer these questions. Choose the best answer.
Circle the letter next to your choice.

1. **A *community* is —**
   A. a place where friends meet to talk
   B. a group of people who live in the same place
   C. people who make things to sell
   D. some people traveling on a bus together

2. **Who makes laws in a community?**
   A. the school principal
   B. firefighters
   C. the oldest members of a community
   D. members of the community government

3. **In which part of the United States is Jacksonville, Florida?**
   A. the north   C. the central
   B. the west   D. the south

4. **Which of the following jobs would you find people doing at Jacksonville's port?**
   A. selling airplane tickets
   B. building and repairing ships
   C. putting food in cans
   D. working at the zoo

5. **Which place might you visit in Jacksonville, Florida?**
   A. the Pacific Ocean
   B. Times Square
   C. the St. Johns River
   D. the Alamo

Name _____   Date _____

Vocabulary Skill: Getting Meaning from Context

Where Do We Build Communities?

When you come across new words as you are reading, you can often use context clues to figure out their meanings. Context clues are clues to a word's meaning. You can find context clues in words, sentences, or pictures. Here is an example from paragraph 1 on page 21:

The phrase *drink fresh water and use it to water the plants* can help you figure out what fresh water is. What is fresh water?

1. Fresh water is _____

_____

Reread the lesson about where people build communities. Think about the meaning of these words.

valley   plain   weather

2–4. Look for context clues in paragraphs, captions, and pictures in the lesson. Then complete the chart.

Word	Clues to meaning	Meaning
valley	• photograph of a California valley • located between mountains and hills	
plain	• photograph of Kansas plain • land is flat or gently rolling	
weather		

Name _____ Date _____

Where Do We Build Communities?

Review pages 20–25 to answer these questions. Choose the best answer.
Circle the letter next to your choice.

1. **Mountains and valleys are examples of —**
   A. landforms   C. ports
   B. hills   D. deserts

2. **Why might people live in mountain communities?**
   A. because they like flat land
   B. because they are surrounded by water
   C. to grow crops such as tomatoes and corn
   D. to work in a ski town

3. **Wichita, Kansas, is located on —**
   A. the seashore
   B. the Pacific Ocean
   C. a plain
   D. a plateau

4. **What is an island?**
   A. flat or gently rolling land
   B. a body of land surrounded by water
   C. an area of low land between mountains and hills
   D. a high area of land

5. **What does *climate* mean?**
   A. the number of mountains in an area
   B. temperature and how much rain or snow an area gets over a
      long period
   C. how cold a community gets in one day
   D. how much snow a community gets in one day

Name _____ Date _____

Environment and Society

How Does Climate Affect a Community?

A climate map shows you what the climate is in different parts of the United States.

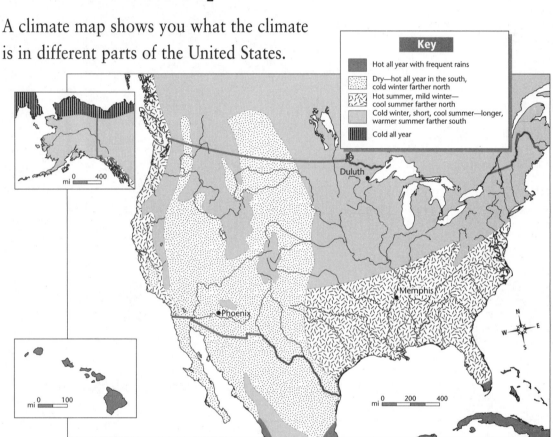

Key

- Hot all year with frequent rains
- Dry—hot all year in the south, cold winter farther north
- Hot summer, mild winter—cool summer farther north
- Cold winter, short, cool summer—longer, warmer summer farther south
- Cold all year

Duluth

Memphis

Phoenix

Use the map above to answer the following questions.

1. **Name a city that has a hot, dry climate.** _____

2. **Name a city that has a cold climate.** _____

3. **Describe your community's climate. Does one of the cities on the map share the climate of your community?**

   _____

   _____

Think Like a Geographer

Workbook for Reading and Review   **9**

Name _____   Date _____

Climate in the United States

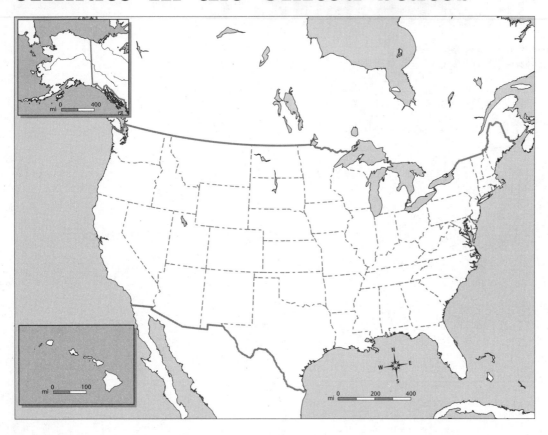

Refer to the climate map on page 26 of your textbook to answer the following questions.

1. **On the map above, create your own climate map and map key. Use colors to show the different climates found in the United States.**

2. **Label the location of your state and community on the map.**

3. **Choose a city in another climate and label it on the map. Based on the climate, would you want to live there? Explain your answer.**

_____

_____

Name _____ Date _____

Vocabulary Skill: Using a Dictionary

This Land of Ours

A dictionary can help you learn what a word means. The words in a dictionary appear in alphabetical order. Guide words at the top of each page help you find the words you are looking for.

The words *coach* and *coat* are guide words. The word *coast* comes after *coach* and before *coat*.

> **coach / coat**
>
> coach (kohch) *v. to teach or train.*
>
> coast (kohst) *n.*

Read how the words in the chart are used in the lesson. Then look up the words in a dictionary and complete the chart.

Words	Guide words	Meaning
1. coast (page 28)		
2. peak (page 29)		
3. grassland (page 29)		
4. feature (page 29)		
5. steep (page 30)		

Name _____ Date _____

This Land of Ours

Read pages 28–31 to answer these questions. Choose the best answer.
Circle the letter next to your choice.

1. **What do *geographers* study?**
   A. the moon, the stars, and the planets
   B. the human body
   C. different landforms of the earth and their locations
   D. none of the above

2. **What landform region do the states of Arkansas, Missouri, and Oklahoma share?**
   A. the Ozark Plateau   C. the Grand Canyon
   B. Great Salt Lake   D. the Colorado Plateau

3. **What are the two main plains areas in the central United States?**
   A. the Coastal Plains and the Rockies
   B. the Appalachians and the Rockies
   C. the Great Plains and the Appalachians
   D. the Central Plains and the Great Plains

4. **In which area of the United States can you find the Pacific Ranges?**
   A. on the West Coast   C. south of the Ozark Plateau
   B. on the East Coast   D. north of the Great Lakes

5. **Which of the following landform regions is west of the Great Plains?**
   A. the Rocky Mountains
   B. the Coastal Plains
   C. the Ozark Plateau
   D. the Appalachian Mountains

Name _____ Date _____

Finding Your Global Address

Your Place in the World

Read the global address below:

1500 Park Street

Charleston

South Carolina

United States

North America

Earth

1. **Which part of the global address is the state?**

   _____

2. **Which part of the global address is the city?**

   _____

3. **Name two states near your state. Look at the map of the United States on pages 346–347 of your book if you need to.**

   _____

   _____

4. **Do people living in these two states have the same global address as you do? Why or why not?**

   _____

   _____

Name _____ Date _____

Finding Your Global Address

Where in the World Are You?

Your global address is made up of your street address, your city, your state, your country, your continent, and your planet.

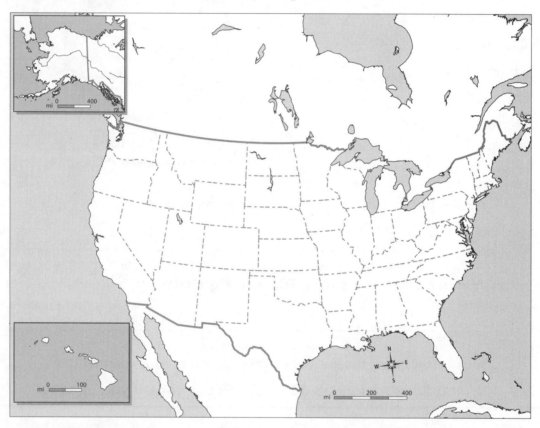

1. **Label your community and state on the map above.**

2. **Name 2 cities you know.** _____

3. **Name 2 states you know.** _____

4. **Name 2 countries you know.** _____

5. **Find Oklahoma and Kentucky on the map and color them in.**

6. **If your friend lives in the capital of Oklahoma, which parts of his or her global address will be different from yours?**

    _____

Chapter 1

Name _____ Date _____

What Is a Community?

Read pages 12–33 to answer these questions. Choose the best answer.
Circle the letter next to your choice.

1. Which of the following can be a community?

A. a bus trip

B. a small town

C. an art museum

D. a supermarket

2. What is a *law*?

A. money people pay to the government

B. a rule that people follow to keep order and stay safe

C. a drawing of a place that shows where things are

D. something that people buy or sell

3. To *elect* means to —

A. stay safe

B. make laws

C. choose by voting

D. build roads and schools

4. Jacksonville's eastern border is —

A. the Atlantic Ocean

B. the St. Johns River

C. the Mississippi River

D. the Colorado River

5. The position of a place on the earth's surface is a —

A. home   C. planet

B. street address   D. location

© Houghton Mifflin Company. All rights reserved/3

Chapter Review   Workbook for Reading and Review   15

Name _____   Date _____

6. **Why might people live by the ocean?**

   A. because they like to swim

   B. because they make a living catching and selling fish

   C. because they work building and repairing ships

   D. all of the above

7. **Why do many communities lie in valleys?**

   A. The flat, rich land is good for farming.

   B. The land is high and steep.

   C. People like to dig for gold and silver.

   D. Salt water is always found in valleys.

8. **Temperature and how much rain or snow a community gets over a long period of time is that community's —**

   A. weather

   B. location

   C. geography

   D. climate

9. **Next to the Atlantic Ocean are the—**

   A. Appalachian Mountains

   B. Great Plains

   C. Rocky Mountains

   D. Coastal Plains

10. **What is a *region*?**

   A. a type of law

   B. any area that has one or more features in common

   C. the area that follows the coastline

   D. a flat place on top of a mountain

Name _____ Date _____

Comprehension Skill: Topic, Main Idea, and Supporting Details

Different Types of Communities

The most important idea in a passage is called the **main idea**.
Supporting details give more information about the main idea. The main
idea and three supporting details below are from page 38.

Main idea
People living in urban areas have many choices.

Supporting detail
They can choose among many kinds of jobs.

Supporting detail
They can go to different stores and restaurants.

Supporting detail
They can get around the city in many ways.

1–2. **Reread page 38. Write two supporting details that describe the following main idea.**

Main idea: City people often work together and share ideas.

Supporting detail: _____

Supporting detail: _____

3–5. **Reread page 39. Write the main idea and two details about Chicago. One supporting detail has been given for you.**

Main idea: _____

Supporting detail: _____

Supporting detail: _____

Supporting detail: Chicago has the busiest railroad yards in the United States.

Name _____ Date _____

Different Types of Communities

Review pages 37–43 to answer these questions. Choose the best answer.
Circle the letter next to your choice.

1. **The total number of people living in a place is its —**
    A. city
    B. government
    C. population
    D. community

2. **The world's first skyscraper was built in —**
    A. Chicago, Illinois
    B. New York, New York
    C. Los Angeles, California
    D. Charlotte, North Carolina

3. **Suburbs are found —**
    A. in the country
    B. only along rivers
    C. at the edge of cities
    D. in the middle of large cities

4. **People first moved to suburbs because —**
    A. they wanted to start farms
    B. there were no schools in the cities
    C. there was more traffic than in the city
    D. land was less expensive than in the city

5. **A rural community —**
    A. has lots of traffic
    B. has few people
    C. is at the edge of a big city
    D. is filled with thousands of buildings

Name _____   Date _____

Preparing for an Interview

Getting to Know You

Suppose you were going to interview someone from Chicago, Illinois.

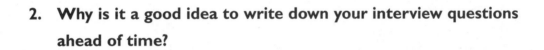

1. **Write three questions you would like to ask that person about living in Chicago.**

    _____

    _____

    _____

2. **Why is it a good idea to write down your interview questions ahead of time?**

    _____

    _____

    _____

3. **What does being prepared for the interview tell the person you are interviewing?**

    _____

    _____

    _____

4. **How could you check that the answers you have written down are what was really said?**

    _____

Name _____ Date _____

Preparing for an Interview

Getting Ready for the Big Interview

What famous person would you most like to interview? A sports star? The President? Another world leader? Answer the questions below to help you plan your interview.

1. **What is the name of the person you would like interview?**

    _____

2. **How would you convince the person to do the interview?**

    _____

    _____

3. **List five questions that you would like to ask during the interview.**

    _____

    _____

    _____

    _____

    _____

4. **Why is it important to have a way of contacting the person after the interview?**

    _____

Name _____ Date _____

Comprehension Skill: Understanding Sequence of Events

A Community at Different Times

Events happen in a certain order, or **sequence**. Time-order words such as *first*, *next*, and *later* can help you figure out that sequence.

In Lesson 2, you read about how Tucson, Arizona, became a part of the United States. The first four events are listed in order below.

1. Native Americans lived and farmed around the Tucson area.
2. The Spanish arrived and claimed the area, calling it Mexico.
3. Father Kino built a mission.
4. The Spanish built a fort at Tucson.

1. **The events below explain how Tucson, Arizona, has changed over time, but they are out of order. Reread pages 47–48. Number the events from 1 to 4 to show the right sequence.**

___ The United States bought land from Mexico.
___ The first public school opened in Tucson.
___ The railroad came to Tucson.
___ Mexico won its freedom from Spain.

2. **Now read page 49 to help you put these events in order.**

___ Air conditioning was invented.
___ People in Tucson built their homes out of mud bricks.
___ Skyscrapers began to be built in Tucson.

3. **Reread the first paragraph on page 47. What time-order words did you find?**

_____

Name _____ Date _____

A Community at Different Times

Review pages 45–49 to answer these questions. Choose the best answer.
Circle the letter next to your choice.

1. **The study of the past is called —**
   A. history
   B. population
   C. geography
   D. transportation

2. **What is a *fort*?**
   A. the total number of people living in a certain place
   B. an area or buildings surrounded by walls
   C. a place where people teach their religion to others
   D. a way to move people and supplies from place to place

3. **People in Tucson tried to make money by —**
   A. ranching
   B. planting rice
   C. building railroad cars
   D. cutting down Tucson's forests

4. **Which is NOT a way the railroad helped Tucson?**
   A. It carried supplies from other places to Tucson.
   B. It made getting people to and from Tucson much easier.
   C. It put all other forms of transportation out of business.
   D. It carried Tucson cattle and copper to other parts of the country.

5. **Which event made it easier for people to live in Tucson?**
   A. the discovery of copper around Tucson
   B. the building of the Spanish mission
   C. the opening of Tucson's first public school
   D. the invention of air conditioning

Name _____ Date _____

Comprehension Skill: Summarizing

Communities Share Many Things

Writing a **summary** of what you have read can help you remember important ideas. When you **summarize**, you retell the important ideas in your own words. Here is a summary of page 58:

> Many different people live in the United States. Each group has its own culture. Their culture includes their religious beliefs, foods, and language.

1–3. Now read pages 62 and 63. As you read, answer the questions in the chart below.

What is this section about?	national holidays in the United States
What is a national holiday?	
What are some ways people celebrate national holidays?	
Which November holiday honors men and women who fought in wars?	

4. Write several sentences that summarize what you read. Use your notes in the chart to help you.

_____

_____

Name _____ Date _____

Communities Share Many Things

Review pages 58–63 to answer these questions. Choose the best answer.
Circle the letter next to your choice.

1. **What is a *culture*?**
    A. a community at the edge of a city
    B. the way of life of a group of people
    C. a person who moves to a new place
    D. the way things are moved from place to place

2. **Shaking hands when you meet is an example of a —**
    A. custom
    B. suburb
    C. settler
    D. national holiday

3. **The powwow held every year in Tulsa, Oklahoma, has become a —**
    A. fort   C. mission
    B. culture   D. tradition

4. **The Scottish Games and Gathering takes place in —**
    A. Chicago, Illinois
    B. Tucson, Arizona
    C. Tulsa, Oklahoma
    D. Los Angeles, California

5. **Veterans Day honors men and women who —**
    A. built the railroads
    B. started important traditions
    C. settled in the United States
    D. fought in wars for the United States

Name _____ Date _____

Communities Are Different and Alike

Review pages 37–63 to answer these questions. Choose the best answer.
Circle the letter next to your choice.

1. **Which is an example of an urban community?**
   A. a shopping mall
   B. a farm with many animals
   C. a large school with lots of students
   D. a city with many people and buildings

2. **Which is NOT a reason Chicago, Illinois, is a good place for business?**
   A. its location
   B. its traffic jams
   C. its railroad system
   D. its large, busy airport

3. **A community at the edge of city is called a —**
   A. rural area   C. suburb
   B. mission   D. town

4. **What are some features of a rural area?**
   A. few people and lots of open space
   B. busy streets and highways
   C. many people and things to do
   D. skyscrapers and apartment buildings

5. **Tucson, Arizona, is located —**
   A. on a plain
   B. in a desert
   C. on an island
   D. beside Lake Michigan

Name _____ Date _____

6. **Which country claimed the area around Tucson long ago?**

   A. France

   B. Spain

   C. England

   D. Germany

7. **Which of the following is still found around Tucson today?**

   A. coal

   B. salt

   C. copper

   D. diamonds

8. **A group's culture includes its —**

   A. missions and forts

   B. population and jobs

   C. transportation and geography

   D. customs and traditions

9. **Two cultural celebrations held in Tulsa, Oklahoma, are a —**

   A. Native American powwow and a Scottish festival

   B. hot-air balloon race and international dance contest

   C. Thanksgiving Day parade and a track-and-field day

   D. city-wide spelling bee and an apple-picking contest

10. **A day set aside to honor or celebrate an event or to honor a person special to our country is called a —**

    A. culture

    B. tradition

    C. religious holiday

    D. national holiday

Name _____ Date _____

Study Skill: Examining Visuals and Captions as Part of Previewing

Native American Communities

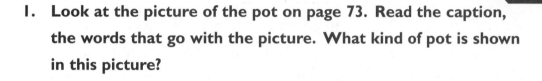

Looking ahead at, or previewing, drawings, photos, and captions
gives you an idea of what you will learn in your lesson.

1. **Look at the picture of the pot on page 73. Read the caption,
   the words that go with the picture. What kind of pot is shown
   in this picture?**

   _____

2. **Now look at the drawing on pages 74 and 75 and read the
   captions. What does the picture show?**

   _____

3. **Look at the drawing on page 78. Read the caption, too. What
   does the drawing show?**

   _____

4. **Who made the pot shown on page 78?**

   _____

5. **What does the picture on page 80 show?**

   _____

6. **Based on your preview, what will you learn about in Lesson 1?**

   _____

   _____

   _____

Name _____ Date _____

Native American Communities

Review pages 73–81 to answer these questions. Choose the best answer.
Circle the letter next to your choice.

1. **Who are the Iroquois?**
   A. people who make and sell pots made of mud and clay
   B. a Native American group that lives in North America
   C. a group of people who came from Europe to America
   D. a group of children who sing, dance, and act out stories

2. **The early Iroquois lived in —**
   A. prairies
   B. deserts
   C. jungles
   D. forests

3. **To *adapt* means —**
   A. to change   C. to play
   B. to work   D. to share

4. **What is a *long house*?**
   A. a house that is as long as a football field
   B. a home built by the Iroquois where ten or more families lived
   C. a house built by the Iroquois that took a very long time to build
   D. another name for any kind of home built a long time ago

5. **What was a group of long houses called?**
   A. a village
   B. a fort
   C. a pueblo
   D. a surrounding

Name _____ Date _____

Comprehension Skill: Understanding Text Organization—General

Settlers in Jamestown

Good writers put facts in an order that is easy for readers to understand. Figuring out how a writer has organized the facts can help you read well. Here are two different ways facts are often organized:

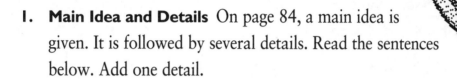

1. **Main Idea and Details** On page 84, a main idea is given. It is followed by several details. Read the sentences below. Add one detail.

   Main Idea: Every community has a story of how it started.

   Detail: The history of Jamestown begins with the many Native Americans who lived there.

   Detail: Then about 400 years ago, some new people came.

   Detail: These people were settlers from England, a country across the Atlantic Ocean.

   Detail: _____

2. **Problem/Solution** On pages 86 and 87, the writer describes the problems the settlers had when they first moved to Jamestown. Then the writer describes the solution. Write the problem and solution below.

   Problem _____

   _____

   Solution _____

Name _____ Date _____

Settlers in Jamestown

Review pages 84–89 to answer these questions. Choose the best answer.
Circle the letter next to your choice.

1. **What is a *settler*?**
   A. a soldier who helped John Smith protect Jamestown
   B. someone who looks for gold and pearls in a new land
   C. a person who goes to a new place to start a community
   D. one who discovers buried treasure from long ago

2. **What did English settlers find along the James River?**
   A. strange plants and animals
   B. gold, silver, and rare jewels
   C. helmets that had been worn long ago
   D. paintings of the King of England

3. **What is a *colony*?**
   A. people who live together in the same area
   B. persons who buy and sell things to make money
   C. a group of people who settle in another land
   D. an area within a state that has its own government

4. **Who was Pocahontas?**
   A. the first early settler in Jamestown to die of starvation
   B. the Native American wife of a settler
   C. someone who showed the settlers how to grow tobacco
   D. all of the above

5. **What is a *fort*?**
   A. a building where people use machines to make things
   B. an area of buildings surrounded by walls for protection
   C. a drawing of a place that shows where things are
   D. a place on river, lake, or ocean where boats can dock

Name _____ Date _____

Comprehension Skill: Noting Details

Salem Takes to the Sea

As you read a history book, pay attention to the facts and descriptions in each paragraph. These **details** help you learn about life in the past.

Read the section called "Down to the Sea in Ships" on pages 91–93.

1. **Write a short answer to this question: "Why was the sea important in Salem's early history?"**

   _____

   _____

Now reread pages 91–93. Then answer these questions:

2. **What did the people of Salem do with the fish they caught?**

   _____

3. **What did Salem merchants send by ship to other countries?**

   _____

Now read the section called "Teapots and Thread" on pages 94 and 95.

4. **What did ships from other countries send to Salem?**

   _____

5. **Pretend you could go back in time and take a walk on a Salem wharf. Use details to write a sentence about what you might find.**

   _____

   _____

Name _____ Date _____

Salem Takes to the Sea

Review pages 90–95 to answer these questions. Choose the best answer.
Circle the letter next to your choice.

1. **What did Salem get from Spain?**
   A. oranges, raisins, and silk handkerchiefs
   B. chocolate, coffee, and tea
   C. sheep, cows, horses, and other livestock
   D. tobacco, peanuts, china teacups, and thread

2. **How was the location of Salem important?**
   A. Salem was near the plains, so the people could grow many grains.
   B. People fished and traded because it was located on the ocean.
   C. There were many bridges that connected Salem to other towns.
   D. The railroad began in Salem and led to towns all over the United States.

3. **What is *cargo*?**
   A. things a ship carries
   B. cars that take things from place to place
   C. a chest of drawers that a sailor owns
   D. tools that a sailor makes to fix torn sails

4. **What is a *merchant*?**
   A. a person who helps make laws
   B. someone who sails around the world to find new land
   C. a young person who works for a sea captain
   D. someone who buys and sells things to make money

5. **How did the people of Salem trade?**
   A. by plane   C. by train
   B. by car   D. by ship

Name _____ Date _____

Understanding Timelines
Get in Line

A timeline can tell you about events that happened in different times
and places. By looking at a timeline, you can see how events are related.
The timeline below tells you about three different communities of
people: the Iroquois, the settlers in Jamestown, and the people of Salem.

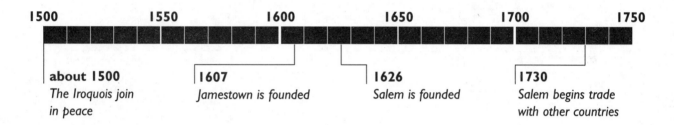

| 1500 | 1550 | 1600 | 1650 | 1700 | 1750 |

about 1500
*The Iroquois join
in peace*

1607
Jamestown is founded

1626
Salem is founded

1730
*Salem begins trade
with other countries*

1. **Which happened first, the founding of Jamestown or the
    founding of Salem?**

    _____

2. **The first Africans came to Jamestown in 1619. Between which
    two events on the timeline would you place this event?**

    _____

    _____

3. **About how much time passed between the time Salem was
    founded and the time it began trading with other countries?**

    _____

4. **What would you have to do to add the start of the Civil War
    in 1861 to this timeline?**

    _____

Name _____ Date _____

Understanding Timelines
A School–Day Timeline

You can make your own timeline to show important events that happen
in your school or classroom. Here's how.

1. **On the lines below, make a list of important events that happen
    on a regular school day. Next to each event, write the time the
    event takes place.**

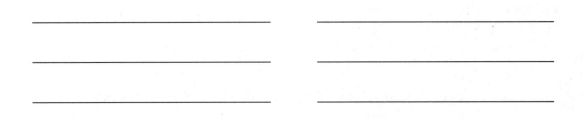

2. **On a long sheet of paper, draw your timeline. Use a ruler to
    measure your timeline. Divide it into equal time periods, such
    as one-, two-, or three- hour blocks.**

3. **Write a title for your timeline. Fill in the times and briefly
    describe the events.**

4. **Decorate your timeline with pictures that show some of
    the events.**

Name _____ Date _____

Early America

Review pages 72–95 to answer these questions. Choose the best answer.
Circle the letter next to your choice.

1. **How did the Iroquois help each other?**
   A. They gave toys and gifts to each other often.
   B. They taught each other how to read and write.
   C. They worked and lived together in a community.
   D. They moved away when someone got sick and died.

2. **Who was Hiawatha?**
   A. a brave Indian girl who helped the animals
   B. an honored Iroquois leader who spoke of peace
   C. the builder of the first long house
   D. a Native American who worked for the Indian Health Services

3. **Why did Hopi men and boys search many days to find trees?**
   A. to find wood to build their homes
   B. to hunt for the squirrels they ate
   C. to gather fruit for their sweet dishes
   D. to get leaves needed to make roofs

4. **What did the Hopi do when they needed more living space?**
   A. moved to a bigger, better space
   B. build another house beside the old one
   C. made a long hall that led to a new building
   D. added a new home on top of the ones there

5. **How was the Iroquois land different from the Hopi land?**
   A. The Iroquois lived by a lake, and the Hopi lived near a river.
   B. The Iroquois grew rice, and the Hopi grew corn.
   C. The Iroquois lived in the woodlands, the Hopi lived in the desert.
   D. The Iroquois used trees for homes, and the Hopi used bricks.

Name _____ Date _____

6. **What did the settlers find along the James River?**

    A. forts and guns

    B. strange animals and plants

    C. gold and pearls

    D. deserts and fields of corn

7. **What did the Powhatan community teach the English settlers about living in a new land?**

    A. how to get to the nearest store

    B. how to make things out of metal

    C. how to hunt, fish, and grow plants

    D. how to use a map to find a treasure

8. **How did the Africans adapt to this new land?**

    A. They learned to plant their own crops and build their own communities.

    B. They showed others how to plant and harvest tobacco.

    C. They brought slaves here to help them do their work.

    D. They made and sold canoes to the Powhatan community.

9. **What did people do to make money in Salem in the 1700s?**

    A. sell fish

    B. sell china teacups

    C. sell thread

    D. sell oranges

10. **What would you probably NOT have seen in Salem in the 1700s?**

    A. carpenters building new ships

    B. farmers growing potatoes and beans

    C. sailors unloading a ship's cargo

    D. wagons loaded with vegetables

Name _____ Date _____

Comprehension Skill: Drawing Conclusions

Native Americans and Newcomers

When you **draw conclusions,** you figure out ideas that go beyond the text.
Use clues from the text and your own knowledge to draw a conclusion.

Here is a conclusion you can draw from page 103 of your textbook:

Clues		What You Know		Conclusion
Settlers had to build their own roads. Log roads were bumpy.	**+**	Building roads is hard work. A long, bumpy ride would not be fun.	**=**	The trip west must have been very hard for settlers.

1. **Reread the third paragraph on page 106. Try to figure out what Dubuque's streets were like at night before 1855. Write your conclusion in the empty box.**

Clues		What You Know		Conclusion
Dubuque had to hire men to watch the streets at night.	**+**	Guards are hired when there is a danger of crime.	**=**	

2–4. **Now reread page 105. Was a miner's job easy or hard? Fill out the chart below using clues from the text.**

Clues		What You Know		Conclusion
	+		**=**	

Name _____ Date _____

Native Americans and Newcomers

Review pages 103–107 to answer these questions. Choose the best
answer. Circle the letter next to your choice.

1. **What did settlers use to make roads?**

    A. straw

    B. bricks

    C. cement

    D. logs

2. **Which way did settlers move to find new land?**

    A. north

    B. west

    C. east

    D. south

3. **Why did settlers build a community in Dubuque?**

    A. Dubuque had lead for mining.

    B. There was plenty of clean water there.

    C. Dubuque had good weather.

    D. They liked living in the desert.

4. **What does *mine* mean?**

    A. to send things to other countries

    B. to dig something out of the earth

    C. to make bullets and paint

    D. to live in the countryside

5. **What is a *mineral*?**

    A. a plant that is grown to be eaten, used, or sold

    B. a nonliving thing in the earth or in water

    C. a place where a plant or animal lives

    D. a bank of dirt that has been raised up

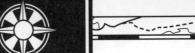

Name _____ Date _____

The Uses of Geography

How Did Settlers Use Rivers as Roads?

Before roads were built, settlers traveled on rivers.
They used flatboats that floated with the river current.

Use the map above to answer the following questions.

1. **You are a settler. You started your flatboat trip at Pittsburgh. Which city will you come to after Cincinnati?**

   _____

2. **Draw the best route from Natchez to Cincinnati.**

Think Like a Geographer   Workbook for Reading and Review   **39**

Name _____   Date _____

From Pittsburgh to New Orleans

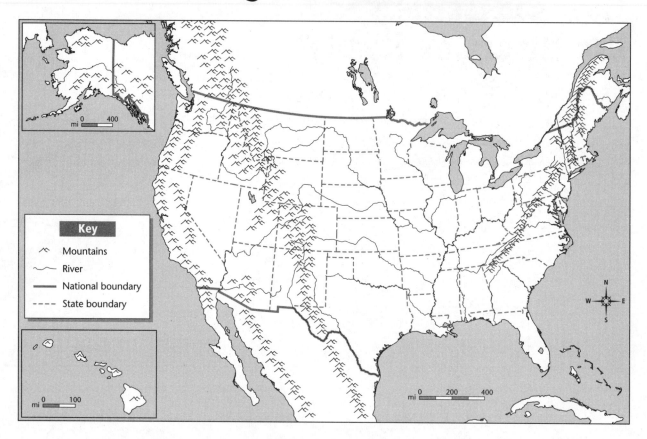

Key
- ⋏⋏ Mountains
- ∿ River
- ━━ National boundary
- - - - State boundary

mi 0 — 400

mi 0 — 100

mi 0 — 200 — 400

Use the map above to answer the following questions.

1. **Many settlers in the 1800s traveled on rivers to get where they wanted to go. Label Pittsburgh and New Orleans.**

2. **Use a pencil to trace the settlers' route by river from Pittsburgh to New Orleans.**

3. **Label the rivers on which they traveled. Use page 109 in your book to help you.**

Name _____ Date _____

Comprehension Skill: Understanding Cause and Effect

From Farms to Factories

A **cause** is an event or condition that makes another event happen. The event that happens is called an **effect.** Here is one cause and one effect from Lesson 2.

Cause ▶	Effect
Power looms replaced hand looms.	People stopped making cloth at home.

Read the following sentences. Figure out which sentence in each pair is the cause and which is the effect. Write the sentences in the boxes where they belong.

1. **The moving wheel makes machine parts move.**
2. **A large wheel turns.**

Cause ▶	Effect

3. **Factories were built in communities.**
4. **People moved to the communities to work in factories.**

Cause ▶	Effect

5. **Many women workers quit their jobs at factories.**
6. **Factory bosses tried to make women workers do more work.**

Cause ▶	Effect

Workbook for Reading and Review   **41**

Name _____ Date _____

From Farms to Factories

Review pages 110–113 to answer these questions. Choose the best answer. Circle the letter next to your choice.

1. **Why did the owners build their mill where they did?**

   A. They built their mill near water to use water power to run their machines.

   B. They needed to have the salt from the ocean to make the food they liked to eat.

   C. They lived near farms where cotton grew, because they needed it to make cloth.

   D. They built it near a college to find good workers for the mill.

2. **What is a _factory_?**

   A. a building where people keep their money and important things

   B. a building where people use machines to make things

   C. a building where people buy and sell things they need

   D. a building with walls around it for protection

3. **A _mill_ is a factory where people make —**

   A. maps   C. radios

   B. books   D. cloth

4. **What kind of work did a young woman do in an urban area in the 1800s?**

   A. work in the fields   C. work in a mill

   B. milk cows and gather eggs   D. work at the library

5. **What is a _boarding house_?**

   A. a house made of boards   C. a house just for mill workers

   B. a hotel   D. a place to sleep in a factory

Name _____ Date _____

Comprehension Strategy: Summarizing
A Wave of Immigrants

As you read, stop from time to time. Think about the most important ideas you have read and write them down. This is called **summarizing**.

Here is a summary of page 114 of Lesson 3.

Millions of immigrants came to the United States. Many came by ship into New York. To them, the Statue of Liberty was a symbol of a new life.

1. **Reread page 115, then circle the best summary.**

    A. Immigrants came to the United States for many reasons. Some people wanted to make a better living. Others wanted religious freedom or to get a good education. The trip was a hard journey, but people came anyway.

    B. The ships were packed with people. The trip often lasted many weeks, and some immigrants got very sick. Many immigrants felt sad because they had to leave family members behind.

2. **Read the rest of Lesson 3. Write a short summary for pages 118–119.**

    _____

    _____

    _____

    _____

Reading and Vocabulary Strategies

Name _____ Date _____

A Wave of Immigrants

Review pages 114–119 to answer these questions. Choose the best
answer. Circle the letter next to your choice.

1. **What greets people when they come to New York City?**

   A. the Grand Canyon   C. the White House

   B. the Statue of Liberty   D. the San Jacinto Monument

2. **What are *immigrants*?**

   A. relatives, like great-grandparents, who have died and left
   things behind

   B. groups of people who study the folklife of different communities

   C. people who leave their homeland to move to a new country

   D. people who can speak and write in many languages

3. **Why did so many people come to the United States in the
   late 1800s and early 1900s?**

   A. They got sick and needed to move to a new place.

   B. They wanted a new and better life.

   C. They wanted to learn to speak English.

   D. They wanted to sail on ships to see a new land.

4. **What is an *ethnic group*?**

   A. people who decide who gets to come into the United States

   B. people who share the same culture

   C. people who bring goods to the United States from other countries

   D. people who sell things to other countries

5. **What was an immigrant neighborhood like?**

   A. Signs were written in the language of their home country.

   B. Farmhouses were built that looked like those in the old country.

   C. Stores sold only food that came from America.

   D. Everyone spoke English instead of their own languages.

Name _____ Date _____

Vocabulary Strategy: Structural Analysis
The Age of the Automobile

When you come to a word you don't know, try breaking it into smaller parts. Here are two ways to break words into smaller parts.

Prefixes are word parts added to the beginning of words.

un means "not" | *sub* means "under"

Circle the prefix in each word below. Then draw a line from each word to its meaning. The first one is done for you.

1. unlicensed   train that travels under the ground

2. subway   not covered with cement

3. unpaved   not having written permission to do something

Suffixes are word parts added to the end of words.

er or *or* means "a person who" | *ly* or *ily* means "in a way that is"

Circle the suffix in each word from Lesson 4 below. Then draw a line from each word to its meaning.

4. planner   in a bad way

5. luckily   a person who visits

6. visitor   a person who plans

7. badly   in a lucky way

Name _____ Date _____

The Age of the Automobile

Review pages 120–125 to answer these questions. Choose the best answer. Circle the letter next to your choice.

1. **What is *technology*?**
   A. land that is part of another community
   B. what people use to travel from one place to another
   C. a community inside a large city
   D. the use of science to make something

2. **What was Atlanta like when the first cars arrived?**
   A. Mr. Steele opened the first car factory.
   B. Streets were made of dirt.
   C. Atlanta was a large, busy city.
   D. There were many schools, stores, and churches all over town.

3. **What is a *license*?**
   A. money paid to take care of the roads
   B. a law passed to make driving safe
   C. how much it costs to drive a car
   D. written permission to do something

4. **What did cars change?**
   A. the kinds of clothing people wore
   B. the kind of work many people did
   C. the music that people listened to
   D. the way that people used their free time

5. **Streetcars were —**
   A. much faster than cars
   B. much slower than cars
   C. made to run on rails down the middle of the street
   D. were narrow and could not seat many people at one time

Name _____ Date _____

Using a Road Map to Find Distance

Hit the Road

A road map is the perfect tool for travelers. It helps them to get from one place to another. A map can also tell how far away places are.

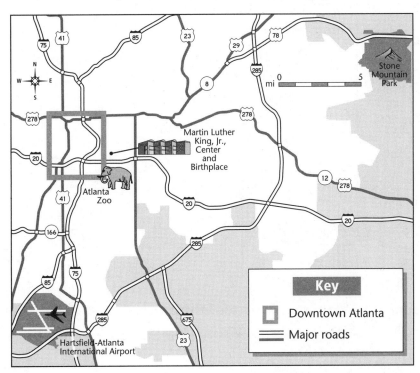

1. **What map symbol is used for the Atlanta Zoo on this map?**

   _____

2. **Find a route from the airport to MLK, Jr., Center. Use string and a ruler to measure that route. How far is it?**

   _____

3. **This symbol** ⬡ **stands for interstate highways. Name two interstate highways that cross in downtown Atlanta.**

   _____

Name _____   Date _____

Using a Road Map to Find Distance

A Ride on Interstate Highway 75

The word *interstate* has two parts: *inter-* meaning "between or among" and *state*. So, interstate highways go between states. Interstate Highway 75 (I-75) runs north and south through six states, from Florida to Michigan. Find I-75 on the map of Detroit.

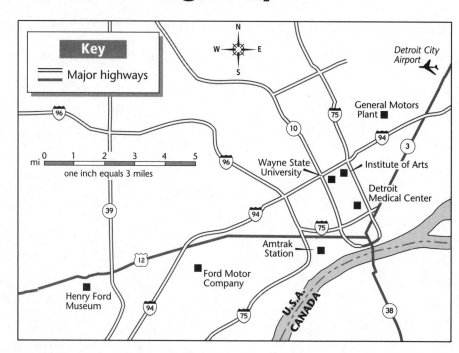

1. **Find a route from the Amtrak Station to the Institute of Arts. Use string and a ruler to measure the distance. How far is it?**

    _____

    _____

2. **What is about 5 miles north of the Detroit Medical Center on Route 3?**

    _____

3. **How far is it from Wayne State University to the Henry Ford Museum?**

    _____

4. **On the map, circle one of the car companies in Detroit.**

Name _____ Date _____

A Growing America

Review pages 102–125 to answer these questions. Choose the best answer. Circle the letter next to your choice.

1. Who were the Mesquakie?

    A. Native Americans who lived in what is now Iowa

    B. miners who worked in Iowa

    C. settlers from Dubuque

    D. relatives of Julien Dubuque

2. What is one way that Dubuque changed during the 1800s?

    A. Shopping malls were built.

    B. People sold their farms.

    C. A fire department was formed.

    D. Telephones were first used.

3. How did factories change the way people lived?

    A. People had more free time.

    B. People left their farms to work in factories.

    C. People worked with their hands to make things.

    D. People helped their family members and neighbors.

4. Why were rivers important to mill owners in early America?

    A. Rivers provided the water to grow their plants.

    B. Mills used water power to run the machines.

    C. Boats carried their goods to other places on rivers.

    D. Mill owners needed water from the rivers to drink.

5. How did Atlanta deal with the problems that cars created?

    A. Atlanta only let a small number of people own cars.

    B. People had to pay money to drive their cars on the roads.

    C. Cars were not allowed to be driven in some neighborhoods.

    D. Wider and better roads were built to help traffic.

Name _____ Date _____

6. **How are immigrants today different from those in the late 1800s?**

   A. Today immigrants want religious freedom.

   B. Today, fewer immigrants come from Europe than in the past.

   C. Today immigrants want better jobs.

   D. Today immigrants want better lives for their families.

7. **Most people who moved to the United States between 1890 and 1920 came from —**

   A. the Caribbean

   B. Asia

   C. Europe

   D. Africa

8. **If you moved to another country, what problems might you face?**

   A. learning a new language

   B. eating different foods

   C. getting around a new place

   D. all of the above

9. **What is an *expressway*?**

   A. a place to buy gas with a credit card

   B. a wide highway built for high-speed travel

   C. a way to travel from place to place in a neighborhood

   D. a way of communicating that connects one town with another

10. **How did rapid transit make life in cities better?**

   A. People bought more cars and trucks.

   B. New and better roads were built.

   C. People could get more done faster.

   D. It was easier for people to get to work.

Name _____ Date _____

Comprehension Skill: Taking Notes
A City and Its Forest

Taking notes can help you remember what you read.
Taking notes means writing down words or phrases that
sum up main ideas and details. Here are some notes for page
139 of Lesson 1.

Page 139   Portland, Oregon
            -trees, orchards, fields cover ground
            -forests, farms, rivers all part of environment
            -all communities have an environment

Now try taking notes yourself. Read Lesson 1. Stop after reading each
passage and write some words or phrases that sum up the information.

1. Resources of Portland—page 140

_____

_____

2. How a Tree Becomes a House—page 142

_____

_____

3. A Center for Lumber—page 143

_____

_____

_____

Name _____ Date _____

A City and Its Forest

Review pages 139–143 to answer these questions. Choose the best answer. Circle the letter next to your choice.

1. What is an *environment*?

    A. the way people communicate with each other

    B. the kind of food people like to eat

    C. the school where you go to learn

    D. the natural world around us

2. What is a *natural resource*?

    A. something that can easily be made by people

    B. anything found by wild animals for food

    C. anything found in the environment that people use

    D. something people use to travel from place to place

3. What natural resources do the people of Portland use?

    A. rich soil, rivers, and forests

    B. sand, wind, and oil

    C. flowers, corn, and potatoes

    D. cactus, rocks, and lakes

4. What is a *port*?

    A. a place where trees are made into wooden houses

    B. another name for a farm stand where vegetables are sold in Portland

    C. a good area for farming, which is why this city is called Portland

    D. a place on a river, lake, or ocean where boats can dock

5. Where is Portland?

    A. in Washington   C. in California

    B. in Oregon   D. in Nevada

Name _____ Date _____

Places and Regions

What's Life Like in a Different Place?

Different resources occur in different regions. The
Yup'ik people in Alaska live along the Yukon River.

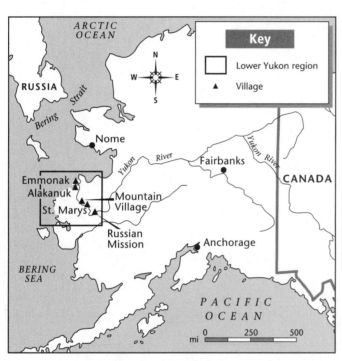

Use the map above to answer the following questions.

1. **Name the communities located in the lower Yukon region.**

   _____

2. **Which other city in Alaska is along a river?**

   _____

3. **What resources can the Yup'ik get from the river?**

   _____

Think Like a Geographer

Name _____   Date _____

Where Is Mexico City?

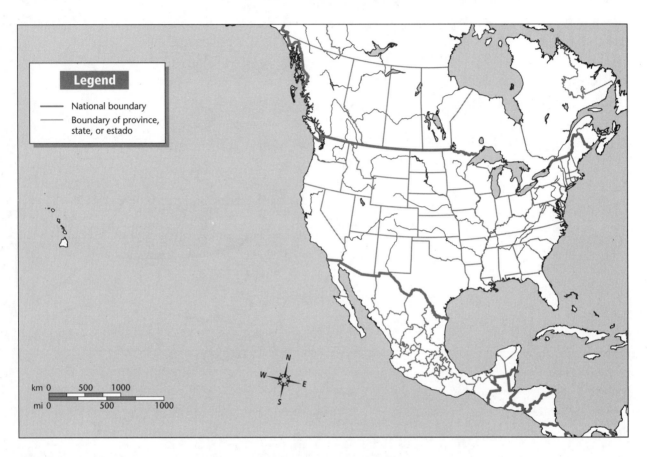

Use the map above to answer the following questions.

1. **Mexico City is the capital of Mexico. Label Mexico City.**

2. **Label the state closest to Mexico City.**

3. **Use a red pen to trace the Rio Grande. Use page 172 to help you.**

Name _____ Date _____

Comprehension Skill: Making Generalizations

A River Community

A **generalization** is a statement that is broadly true. To make a generalization, start with a group of facts. Then think of a statement that is true for all of the facts. Here is an example.

Fact
Forests are important to Portland, Oregon.

Fact
Rich farmland is important to Greenville, Mississippi.

Fact
Portland and Greenville use their ports for shipping.

Generalization: Natural resources are important to a community.

1. **Read these facts. Then circle the generalization that is true for all three facts.**

Fact
Fishermen catch fish in the Mississippi River.

Fact
Factories use the Mississippi for transportation.

Fact
Farmers grow crops on land near the Mississippi.

A. Rich farmland is found near the Mississippi River.

B. Many people who live on the Mississippi depend on the river.

2. **Now reread pages 152–154, beginning with "Raging River." Circle the generalization that fits all the facts.**

A. People build walls from sandbags.

B. Communities work together to prepare for floods.

3. **What else could you say about people who live near rivers that flood? Write your own generalization here.**

_____

_____

Name _____ Date _____

A River Community

Review pages 150–155 to answer these questions. Choose the best
answer. Circle the letter next to your choice.

1. **What kind of large boat takes people on the river to have fun?**

   A. a canoe   C. a tugboat

   B. a rowboat   D. a paddlewheeler

2. **Which is NOT a way people who live in communities along
   the Mississippi use the river?**

   A. for transportation

   B. for farming

   C. for fishing

   D. for whaling

3. **What is** *agriculture*?

   A. fishing

   B. hunting

   C. farming

   D. selling

4. **What is** *silt*?

   A. things in the water which harm plants, animals, or people

   B. fine particles of dirt which make the soil fertile

   C. a place where people buy and sell things they need

   D. a way to grow plants to make them bigger and healthier

5. **What is a** *crop*?

   A. a plant that is grown to be used, eaten, or sold

   B. a product that is made to be sold

   C. a sandbag used to stop floodwaters

   D. a community just outside of a city

Name _____ Date _____

Using Diagrams

The Power of Water

People who live near rivers sometimes need to be prepared for floods. If you lived near a river, you and your family might keep food supplies, drinking water, flashlights, and a radio on hand. This diagram is from the back of a radio. It shows how to replace the batteries.

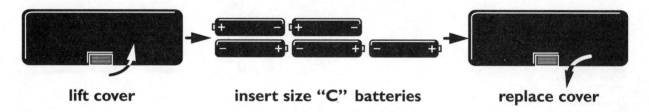

lift cover   insert size "C" batteries   replace cover

1. **How do you know what this diagram is about?**

   _____

2. **What is the first thing to do when replacing batteries?**

   _____

3. **According to the diagram, how many batteries will you need to make this radio work?**

   _____

4. **The diagram tells you to use size "C" batteries. What else does it tell you about the batteries?**

   _____

5. **Why is it a good idea to have a diagram printed on the radio instead of written directions on a sheet of paper?**

   _____

Name _____ Date _____

Using Diagrams

How Does It Work?

1. **Choose one activity below. In the space, draw a diagram with at least three steps showing how to do the activity. Use arrows to show in what order things are done.**

____ Sharpen a pencil.   ____ Make toast.

____ Start up a computer.   ____ Feed a pet.

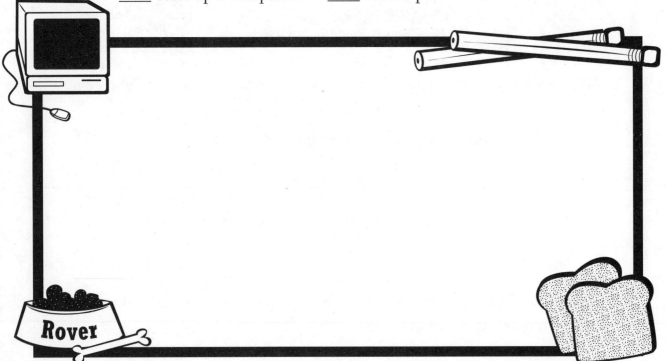

2. **On the lines below, use words to tell how to do the activity**

   you chose. _____

   _____

   _____

3. **Which is more helpful, drawing a diagram or using words to explain**

   your activity? _____

Name _____ Date _____

Using America's Resources

Review pages 138–155 to answer these questions. Choose the best
answer. Circle the letter next to your choice.

1. **What might you see if you flew in an airplane near Portland?**

   A. deserts, mountains,   C. bays, shores, and
   and lakes   lowlands

   B. plains, hills, and valleys   D. forests, rivers, and farms

2. **Who was John Muir?**

   A. a farmer from Portland who came up with new ways of farming

   B. someone who helped forests become national parks

   C. a man who planted many trees in Portland to make new forests

   D. the first leader of Portland who started this community long ago

3. **What kind of crops grow well in Portland?**

   A. oranges and lemons

   B. rice, soybeans, and green beans

   C. strawberries and blueberries

   D. potatoes, corn, and wheat

4. **How did the flood of 1927 affect Greenville?**

   A. It gave Mark Twain the idea of writing *The Adventures of
   Tom Sawyer*.

   B. It brought a lot of snow that melted fast.

   C. It helped the cotton crop that year.

   D. It destroyed homes, businesses, and farms.

5. **What natural resource is very important to the people
   of Greenville?**

   A. oil   C. gold

   B. water   D. forests

Name _____ Date _____

6. **Douglas firs are important to the people of Portland because they provide —**
   A. fruit for canning
   B. lumber for building
   C. protection from heavy rains
   D. shade for growing food crops

7. **What landform in Greenville, Mississippi, is important to how people live there?**
   A. the Appalachian Mountains
   B. the Great Lakes
   C. the Mississippi River delta
   D. the Great Plains

8. **What causes flooding in communities near the Mississippi River?**
   A. the biggest river in the world
   B. too many fish in the river
   C. houses that are too low to the ground
   D. melting snow and rain

9. **The people of Greenville helped each other during the flood of 1927 by —**
   A. giving homeless people food and a place to stay
   B. growing rice after the floods and giving it away for free
   C. taking boat rides up and down the Mississippi River
   D. replanting the cotton crop that year

10. **How do the people of Greenville prevent flooding?**
    A. by putting sandbags along the river
    B. by putting extra gutters on their houses
    C. by moving to higher ground
    D. by building up riverbanks to control the river

Name _____ Date _____

Comprehension Strategy: K-W-L

A Community by the Ocean

A **K-W-L** chart can help you understand and remember
what you read. Here are the steps of K-W-L:

K - **Write what you Know.** What is
Lesson 1 about? Write what you
know about the topic in the
first column of the chart.

W - **Write what you Want to learn.**
Write your questions about the topic
in the middle part of the chart.

L - **Write what you Learned.** After
reading the lesson, write what you
learned in the third column of the chart.

Now follow the steps of K-W-L as you read Lesson 1.
You can use this chart.

K — What I Know	W — What I Want to Learn	L — What I Learned

Name _____ Date _____

A Community by the Ocean

Review pages 165–169 to answer these questions. Choose the best
answer. Circle the letter next to your choice.

1. **The United States, Canada, and Mexico are all located on the
   continent of —**
   A. Asia   C. Australia
   B. Europe   D. North America

2. **Nova Scotia, Canada, is a —**
   A. lake
   B. forest
   C. desert
   D. peninsula

3. **A province is like a —**
   A. city
   B. state
   C. country
   D. school district

4. **Which of the following is a resource found near Halifax?**
   A. rice
   B. pearls
   C. forests
   D. pineapples

5. **The amount of a resource that can be used is called its —**
   A. supply
   B. climate
   C. product
   D. container

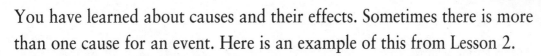

Name _____ Date _____

Comprehension Skill: Understanding Cause and Effect

A City Near the Mountains

You have learned about causes and their effects. Sometimes there is more than one cause for an event. Here is an example of this from Lesson 2.

Causes ▶	Effect
Many people in Mexico City drive cars and trucks. Many people use gas for cooking and heating.	Mexico City's air is very polluted.

1. **Circle a third cause of Mexico City's air pollution.**
   Factory smoke spills into the air.
   Mexico City is built where Tenochtitlán used to be.

2. **Reread the second paragraph on page 173. How does Mexico City's location make its air pollution worse?**

   _____

   _____

3. **Find two causes and one effect. Circle the two causes. Underline the effect.**

   People take the subway instead of driving their cars.

   The air gets a little cleaner.

   Mexico City's new buses give off less pollution.

Reading and Vocabulary Strategies

Name _____ Date _____

A City Near the Mountains

Review pages 170–175 to answer these questions. Choose the best
answer. Circle the letter next to your choice.

1. **Who built the city of Tenochtitlán?**
   A. the Maya   C. the Aztecs
   B. the Incas   D. the Pueblo

2. **How did the people in Tenochtitlán grow crops?**
   A. They planted seeds in the sand, so that some would grow.
   B. They dug small ditches in the ground, and then filled them
      with seeds and water.
   C. They made mounds of dirt, sprinkled seeds on top, and
      flooded them with water.
   D. They built rafts piled with dirt, and the roots of plants held the
      rafts in place.

3. **What is the capital of Mexico?**
   A. Tenochtitlán   C. Mazatlán
   B. Mexico City   D. Veracruz

4. **What is *air pollution*?**
   A. dirt and chemicals in the air that can harm people
   B. the amount of clean air for people to breathe
   C. the direction the air is moving
   D. a way to tell if it is a good day for flying or not

5. **How has population growth affected the air pollution in
   Mexico City?**
   A. As more people move to the city, more factories are built.
   B. More people in the city means more cars and trucks.
   C. Farmers have to grow more crops to feed more people.
   D. Farmers bring clean, fresh air when they move to the city.

Name _____ Date _____

Using Climate and Resource Maps
What Grows Where?

The two maps below show the same part of Canada. One map shows temperature in July and the other shows resources found in Canada. Study the maps and the map keys.

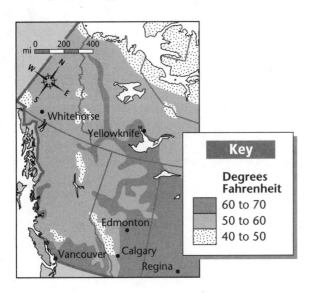 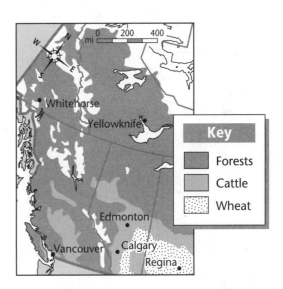

1. **Which city has colder temperatures in July, Whitehorse or Edmonton?**

    _____

2. **Which resource is found around Yellowknife?** _____

3. **What is the average temperature in Vancouver in July?** _____

4. **Which resources are found near Calgary?** _____

    _____

5. **What temperatures are best for growing wheat? How do you know?**

    _____

Name _____ Date _____

Using Climate and Resource Maps

Coffee, Corn, and Sheep

These maps show a part of Mexico. One map shows yearly rainfall. The other shows farm products. Study the maps and map keys to learn about Mexico.

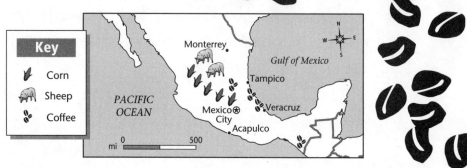

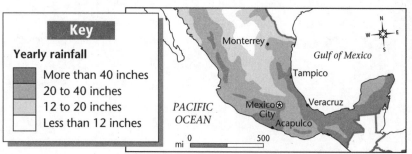

1. **Name two cities that receive more than 40 inches of rain a year.**

   _____

2. **If you were visiting a sheep ranch, which city would you visit?**

   _____

3. **Which city gets less rain each year, Tampico or Monterrey?**

   _____

4. **Which crop do you think needs more rain to grow, corn or coffee? Why do you think so?**

   _____

   _____

Name _____ Date _____

Our North American Neighbors

Review pages 165–175 to answer these questions. Choose the best answer. Circle the letter next to your choice.

1. **Halifax, Nova Scotia, is located near the —**
   A. Arctic Ocean
   B. Atlantic Ocean
   C. Lake Michigan
   D. Mediterranean Sea

2. **The port at Halifax Harbor is —**
   A. closed most of the year
   B. small and poorly built
   C. open only to fishing boats
   D. large and open year-round

3. **Why are the forests around Halifax important to the community?**
   A. They are the best places to find good lobster.
   B. They keep the ocean from flooding Halifax.
   C. They provide wood for boards and wood pulp.
   D. They are good places to graze sheep and cattle.

4. **A place to buy and sell things is a —**
   A. fort   C. market
   B. supply   D. resource

5. **Fish sent across the ocean are packed in —**
   A. barrels   C. plastic bags
   B. sawdust   D. refrigerated containers

Name _____ Date _____

6. **Who first settled the area that is now Mexico City?**

   A. the Aztec

   B. the Incas

   C. the Maya

   D. the Iroquois

7. **How does Mexico City's geography make it a good place to be the capital of Mexico?**

   A. The mountains keep it safe.

   B. It is in the middle of Mexico.

   C. The nearby ocean helps trade.

   D. The forests keep the city cool in summer.

8. **Why do so many people live in Mexico City?**

   A. Many people come for jobs in the city.

   B. There is very little crime in Mexico City.

   C. The air and water are very clean in Mexico City.

   D. Many people go there on vacation and decide to stay.

9. **In winter, the air pollution in Mexico City gets worse because —**

   A. it is the windy season

   B. all of the subways and buses shut down

   C. there is no rain to wash the dirt out of the air

   D. there are more visitors in Mexico City during that time

10. **The government of Mexico City is trying to reduce air pollution by —**

    A. closing down public parks and zoos

    B. building more subways and buying new buses

    C. encouraging more businesses to move to the city

    D. inviting more students to go to school in the city

Chapter Review

Name _____ Date _____

Vocabulary Skill: Technical Terms

Oil Makes Jobs

Special words are often used to talk about certain subjects. In Lesson 1, many special words are used to talk about the oil business. Here are some of the words used on pages 188 and 189.

processed	**gasoline**	**oil derricks**	**polyester**
refined	**fuel**	**oil wells**	**nylon**

Write each word under the sentence that tells about it. Two words go under each sentence. Look at how the words are used in Lesson 1 to help you.

1. **These are kinds of fabric, or cloth.**

   _____

2. **These words tell what a car runs on.**

   _____

3. **These words describe oil that is cleaned.**

   _____

4. **These help people get oil out of the ground.**

   _____

5. **Often you can find clues to the meaning of a difficult word in the sentences around it. Read page 189. Write a sentence telling what an oil boom is.**

   _____

   _____

Name _____ Date _____

Oil Makes Jobs

Review pages 187–191 to answer these questions. Choose the best answer. Circle the letter next to your choice.

1. **Why is oil important to Casper's economy?**
   A. It provides jobs for many people in Casper.
   B. People like to use gasoline to drive their cars and trucks.
   C. Homes are heated by oil to keep them warm.
   D. Casper is the capital of Wyoming.

2. **What happens in an oil boom?**
   A. The demand for oil is high.
   B. People lose their jobs.
   C. People don't need oil anymore.
   D. Cities stop growing.

3. **A refinery can turn oil into —**
   A. paper and cardboard
   B. gasoline and plastics
   C. nails and wire
   D. wood and glass

4. **What do many people in Casper like about their city?**
   A. the crowds
   B. the oil business
   C. the outdoors
   D. the beaches

5. **After the oil boom, people in Casper —**
   A. never bought gasoline from oil companies again
   B. lost their jobs and decided not to get new ones
   C. found new jobs, such as working in banks or raising cattle
   D. spent their time just sledding, hiking, skiing, and camping

Lesson Review

Name _____ Date _____

Study Skill: Examining Visuals as Part of Previewing

History Makes Jobs

Previewing a lesson by looking at maps, pictures, and captions
helps you prepare for reading the lesson. Try previewing Lesson 2.

1. **What is the title of Lesson 2?**

    _____

2. **What is the heading and the Focus question on
    page 194?**

    Heading: _____

    Focus question: _____

3. **What does the map at the bottom of pages 194 and 195 show?**

    _____

    _____

4. **Read the two captions under "A Busy Colonial City" on page
    195. Why do so many people visit Williamsburg each year?**

    _____

5. **Read the caption and look at the picture on page 196. Why do
    you think the man is dressed in the clothes of Colonial times?**

    _____

6. **Now read the other headings, Focus questions, and captions
    for Lesson 2. Also look at the pictures. What do you think you
    will learn about in Lesson 2?**

    _____

Name _____ Date _____

History Makes Jobs

Review pages 194–199 to answer these questions. Choose the best answer. Circle the letter next to your choice.

1. What is a *service*?

   A. work that someone does for other people

   B. someone who is forced to work for others without pay

   C. a community where everyone works together

   D. money paid to the community by visitors

2. What service do people at Colonial Williamsburg provide?

   A. providing clean air and water

   B. teaching visitors about colonial life

   C. making pottery and blowing glass

   D. growing vegetables and fruits

3. What is Williamsburg's resource?

   A. oil   C. its history

   B. the land   D. water

4. How do children learn what to tell visitors to Williamsburg?

   A. Children do not talk to the visitors at Williamsburg, but are silent actors.

   B. They have to read many books and then take a test.

   C. They study a huge book and spend a week learning about the past.

   D. Their parents who work at Williamsburg teach them.

5. Williamsburg was once part of a colony that belonged to —

   A. England

   B. France

   C. Spain

   D. Mexico

Name _____ Date _____

Using Reference Books
Track It Down

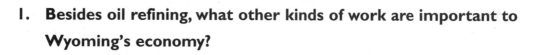

Suppose you wanted to know more
about Wyoming. How would you find
the information? In the spaces below, write
the type of reference book — dictionary or encyclopedia — you would
use to get information about each question. Then write the words
or subjects you would look up.

1. **Besides oil refining, what other kinds of work are important to Wyoming's economy?**

   • Reference book I would use: _____

   • Words or subjects to look up: _____

2. **What is the difference between an oil well and a derrick?**

   • Reference book I would use: _____

   • Words or subjects to look up: _____

3. **Wyoming is an important sheep-raising and wool-producing state. How is wool made?**

   • Reference book I would use: _____

   • Words or subjects to look up: _____

4. **What does *woolen* mean and how do you pronounce it?**

   • Reference book I would use: _____

   • Words or subjects to look up: _____

Name _____ Date _____

Using Reference Books

Learning More About Williamsburg

1776

Liberty Inn

You've read about Colonial Williamsburg in your textbook.
Now you want to do research to learn more about the old town.

1. **Here are some new words you might come across in your reading:** *silversmith, milliner, cabinetmaker, wheelwright.* **What reference book would you use to find out their meanings?**

   _____

2. **Look up the meaning of each word and write it below.**

   silversmith _____

   milliner _____

   cabinetmaker _____

   wheelwright _____

3. **Suppose you worked in Colonial Williamsburg. Which type of business listed in Question 2 would you choose? Why?**

   _____

   _____

   _____

Name _____ Date _____

Americans Working Together

Review pages 187–199 to answer these questions. Choose the best answer. Circle the letter next to your choice.

1. **Which natural resource has helped Casper, Wyoming's, economy the most?**

   A. water

   B. oil

   C. gold

   D. salt

2. **What happened to Casper's economy when people began driving cars in the early 1900s?**

   A. The ranchers who raised cattle for a living lost money.

   B. There was more of a demand for the oil found in Casper.

   C. New automobile factories were built in Casper.

   D. Many people lost their jobs in Casper.

3. **What happened in Casper after the oil boom in the late 1970s?**

   A. Many people moved to Casper to find new jobs.

   B. New restaurants and hotels opened there.

   C. The city of Casper grew very quickly.

   D. People who worked for oil companies lost their jobs.

4. **What kinds of jobs do many people have in Casper today?**

   A. cattle ranching, banking, and sales

   B. car and truck making

   C. hiking, skiing, and sledding

   D. giving tours of the desert

5. **What does *employment* mean?**

   A. what people do for fun

   B. money people save

   C. something people can sell

   D. work people do for a living

Name _____ Date _____

6. **What are *goods*?**

   A. belongings that people took with them on wagons

   B. jobs people have that make or use oil

   C. things that are made or grown to be sold

   D. another name for oil companies that do well

7. **Why do many people visit Colonial Williamsburg?**

   A. to go shopping

   B. to learn about life long ago

   C. to stay in hotels or motels

   D. to go out to dinner

8. **What does *colonial* mean?**

   A. born in Virginia

   B. from another country

   C. living and working together

   D. part of a colony

9. **How did Williamsburg get rebuilt?**

   A. The United States government paid to have it rebuilt.

   B. Many people from Virginia saved their money for years.

   C. John D. Rockefeller, Jr., gave money to save the old part of this city.

   D. The College of William and Mary raised the money.

10. **How do visitors to Williamsburg help this city?**

    A. Many visitors decide to live in Williamsburg.

    B. They spend their money and help create jobs for people who live here.

    C. They become a part of the community and provide services.

    D. They keep the city neat by putting all trash in trash cans and by recycling.

Chapter Review

Name _____ Date _____

Comprehension Skill: Categorizing

A Global Market

Grouping things together that are alike is called **categorizing**. Categorizing can help you understand and remember information.

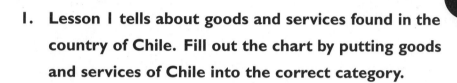

1. **Lesson 1 tells about goods and services found in the country of Chile. Fill out the chart by putting goods and services of Chile into the correct category.**

| grapes | shining shoes | selling tickets |
| driving a bus | box of plums | blackberries |

Goods	Services

2. **Think of two other goods and two services. Add their names to the chart above.**

Name _____ Date _____

A Global Market

Review pages 209–213 to answer these questions. Choose the best answer. Circle the letter next to your choice.

1. **Where is Chile?**

   A. in South Africa

   C. in south Florida

   B. in South America

   D. in southern Europe

2. **How does Chile's weather affect its economy?**

   A. Tourists from all over the world visit Chile's beaches in winter.

   B. People like to go to Chile to ski in January when it is snowing.

   C. Fruit grown in Chile in the winter is sold to people in the United States.

   D. Chile's hot, dry summers make farming there difficult.

3. **Many people in Chile enjoy playing and watching —**

   A. badminton

   B. table tennis

   C. soccer

   D. dodge ball

4. **Which is NOT grown in Chile to sell to other countries?**

   A. grapes

   C. pumpkins

   B. berries

   D. plums

5. **What does *export* mean?**

   A. to buy, sell, or trade goods

   B. to send things to other countries

   C. to leave one's home and go to another country

   D. to bring something in from another country

Lesson Review

Name _____ Date _____

Human Systems

How Do Goods Travel Around the World?

Ships carry goods all around the world.

Use the map below to answer the following questions.

1. **A ship travels from San Francisco, California, to Lima, Peru. On which ocean does the ship travel?**

    _____

2. **A ship goes from Houston, Texas, to Lima, Peru. Use a red crayon to trace the shortest route on the map below.**

3. **Ships bring goods into ports like San Francisco and New York City. What other kinds of transportation are important in port cities? Why?**

    _____

    _____

    _____

    _____

    _____

    _____

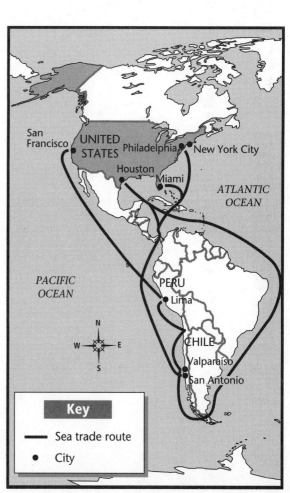

Name _____ Date _____

World Continents and Oceans

Label the seven continents and the four oceans of the world. Use page 222–223 and 342–343 in your book to help you.

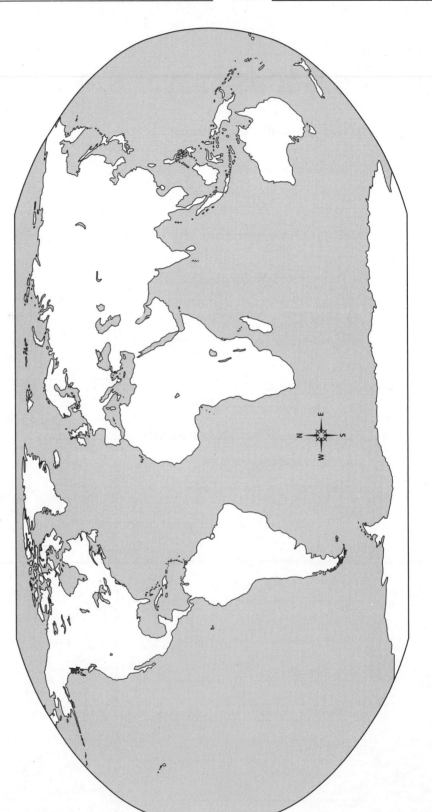

Name _____ Date _____

Comprehension Skill: Taking Notes

An Island Economy

You have learned that **taking notes** helps you remember what you have read. Here are some notes for page 216 of Lesson 2.

Page 216　　　Puerto Rico

　　　　　　　　– a warm island with many visitors

　　　　　　　　– has a busy economy

　　　　　　　　– has modern factories that export goods

　　　　　　　　– important in the economy of North America

Now take notes for the rest of Lesson 2. Stop after reading each page. Write down words and phrases that sum up the information.

1. **Relations with the United States — page 217**

　　_____

　　_____

2. **Puerto Rico's Economy — pages 218–219**

　　_____

　　_____

　　_____

3. **A Smart Shopper — pages 220–221**

　　_____

　　_____

Name _____ Date _____

An Island Economy

Review pages 216–221 to answer these questions. Choose the best answer. Circle the letter next to your choice.

1. **In which body of water is Puerto Rico?**
    A. the Mediterranean Sea
    B. the Pacific Ocean
    C. Lake Michigan
    D. the Caribbean Sea

2. **The two official languages of Puerto Rico are English and —**
    A. Portuguese
    B. Spanish
    C. German
    D. French

3. **What is a *profit*?**
    A. money that a business pays its workers
    B. one of the many natural resources found in Puerto Rico
    C. the amount of money a business earns after it pays its costs
    D. money a business uses to buy materials and machinery

4. **People who provide services may have jobs —**
    A. in banks
    B. mining clay
    C. manufacturing scientific tools
    D. all of the above

5. **A consumer is a person who —**
    A. eats only meat
    B. buys goods and services
    C. sells goods and services
    D. works on computers for a living

Lesson Review

Name _____   Date _____

Understanding Hemispheres
Half a World Away

Study these maps of
the hemispheres.

Northern

Southern

Eastern

Western

1. **Name a continent in the Northern and Eastern Hemispheres.**

    _____

2. **Name a continent in the Southern and Western Hemispheres.**

    _____

3. **Why do you think mapmakers make maps that show hemispheres?**

    _____

Name _____ Date _____

Understanding Hemispheres

GeoQuiz

Study the hemisphere maps on pages 222–223 and the world map on pages 342–343 of your textbook. Then, close your textbook and answer as many of the questions below as you can. Give yourself **20 points** for each correct answer. (Use the hemisphere and world maps in your textbook to check your answers.) Tally your points, then use the scale below to figure out your **GeoSkill**.

100 points = GeoSkill Super Master	40 points = GeoSkill Study-More Master
80 points = GeoSkill Senior Master	20 points = GeoSkill Needs-Help Master
60 points = GeoSkill Junior Master	0 points = Try again another day

1. **In which two hemispheres is North America located?**

_____

2. **Which oceans are located in the Western hemisphere?**

_____

3. **Name the continents that appear in the Western Hemisphere.**

_____

_____

4. **Name a continent located in the Northern and Western hemisphere.**

_____

5. **In which hemisphere or hemispheres do you live?**

_____

Name _____   Date _____

Goods and Services in the Americas

Review pages 208–221 to answer these questions. Choose the best
answer. Circle the letter next to your choice.

1. **Goods from one part of the world being sold in another part is one part of —**
   A. a global market
   B. geography
   C. a community resource
   D. climate

2. **Why does the United States buy fresh fruit from Chile in January?**
   A. Chile grows bigger, better fruit than any other country.
   B. There are more farmers in Chile than in the United States.
   C. There is better transportation in Chile than in America.
   D. January is a summer month in Chile, and a lot of fruit grows during this time.

3. **To make sure fruit does not spoil on the long trip from Chile to the United States, it is —**
   A. chilled   C. put in the sun
   B. wrapped up in big boxes   D. packed in small containers

4. **What is the capital of Chile?**
   A. Valparaíso   C. Santiago
   B. Lima   D. San Antonio

5. **Chile is on the continent of —**
   A. Asia
   B. North America
   C. Europe
   D. South America

Name _____ Date _____

6. **Which of the following describes Puerto Rico?**

   A. Puerto Rico is a state in the United States.

   B. Puerto Rico is a commonwealth of the United States.

   C. Puerto Rico is a territory of the United States.

   D. Puerto Rico is a region of the United States.

7. **What is the capital of Puerto Rico?**

   A. San Juan

   B. Marrakesh

   C. Mexico City

   D. San Diego

8. **An example of a manufacturing job is —**

   A. working as a waiter in a restaurant

   B. selling computers in a store

   C. making clothing in a factory

   D. showing tourists around San Juan

9. **What type of job deals with clay, limestone, and salt found in the ground?**

   A. computer programming

   B. mining

   C. teaching

   D. banking

10. **In looking for a computer, a wise consumer —**

    A. buys the first computer she sees before someone else finds it

    B. thinks carefully and compares prices

    C. buys the most expensive computer because it's always the best

    D. pays for all features in a computer, even if she doesn't need them all

Name _____ Date _____

Comprehension Strategy: Adjust Reading Rate
The Fourth of July

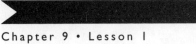

Sometimes reading is fun. Other times
reading is hard work. When you read for fun, you
can read quickly, but you should slow down for harder
books. This is called **adjusting your reading rate.**

I. **Read page 233 quickly. Then read it slowly a second
    time. Which reading helped you understand the
    page better?**

    _____

Now read the section called "Tell Me More" on page 236. Read slowly
and carefully. Then answer each question below in a complete sentence:

2. **Who did the colonies want to be independent from?**

    _____

3. **Why did the colonies want to be independent?**

    _____

4. **What was the Declaration of Independence?**

    _____

5. **Imagine that your class is going to read the Declaration of
    Independence. What would be the best way to read it, quickly
    or slowly? Tell why you think so.**

    _____

    _____

Name _____ Date _____

The Fourth of July

Review pages 233–237 to answer these questions. Choose the best answer. Circle the letter next to your choice.

1. **What is another name for the Fourth of July?**
   A. Memorial Day   C. Veterans Day
   B. Independence Day   D. Summer Vacation Day

2. **What happened on July 4, 1776?**
   A. There was a big fireworks celebration in Philadelphia.
   B. The first President of the United States was elected.
   C. The Declaration of Independence was signed.
   D. The first flag of the United States was made.

3. **Which of the following is a symbol of freedom?**
   A. Washington, D.C.   C. fireworks
   B. the White House   D. the Liberty Bell

4. **How do people celebrate the Fourth of July in Rapid City, South Dakota?**
   A. Cowboys read poems and children have art shows.
   B. All the people in the city meet at the zoo for a big party.
   C. All adults ride horseback down the main street
   D. The city's fire engines are all in a big parade.

5. **What does *heritage* mean?**
   A. the gathering of many bands to perform in a parade
   B. a people's language, beliefs, and customs passed down through generations
   C. a kind of music, such as jazz, country and western, or blues
   D. the original 13 colonies that first made up America

Name _____   Date _____

Using Inset Maps
What's in That Box?

An inset map gives a close-up view of one part of a map. Here are two maps of Washington, D.C. — a large map and a small inset map.

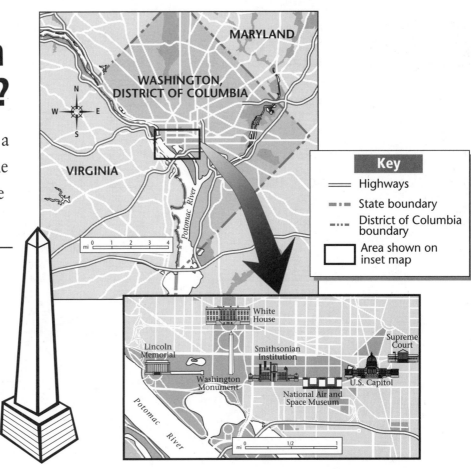

1. **Look at the scales on the large map and on the inset map. How are they different?**

   _____

2. **Suppose your family is driving from Maryland to Washington, D.C., to visit the Smithsonian Institution. Which map will help you find the way?**

   _____

3. **Which map will help you find the best way to walk from the White House to the Smithsonian Institution?**

   _____

Name _____   Date _____

Using Inset Maps
Exploring the Black Hills

There are many places to visit in the Black Hills of South Dakota near Rapid City. Look at the inset map to learn about two of them.

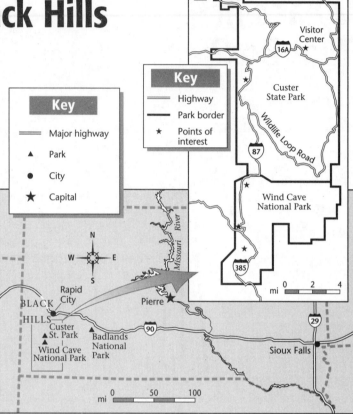

Key

───── Major highway

▲ Park

● City

★ Capital

Key

═══ Highway

▬ Park border

★ Points of interest

1. **What two places are easier to see on the inset map? Why?**

_____

2. **Write a question that the large map could help you answer.**

_____

3. **Write a question that the inset map could help you answer.**

_____

4. **For what other place in South Dakota would an inset map be useful? Explain why.**

_____

_____

Skills Workshop

Name _____ Date _____

Comprehension Strategy: Self-Monitoring

A Rice Festival

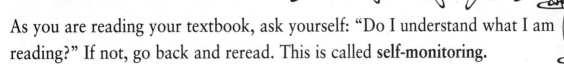

As you are reading your textbook, ask yourself: "Do I understand what I am reading?" If not, go back and reread. This is called **self-monitoring**.

One way you can monitor your reading is to answer the Focus questions. Try this as you read Lesson 2. Write your answers on the lines below.

1. **A Harvest Celebration**

   Focus question: How do the people of Crowley celebrate the natural resource of rice?

   _____

   _____

2. **Cajun Louisiana**

   Focus question: How do Cajuns share their heritage at the Rice Festival?

   _____

   _____

3. **Are there any words or ideas in Lesson 2 that you do not understand? Write them here.**

   _____

   _____

4. **What could you do to understand these words or ideas? List two ways to find out what they mean.**

   _____

   _____

Name _____ Date _____

A Rice Festival

Review pages 242–245 to answer these questions. Choose the best answer. Circle the letter next to your choice.

1. **What is a *harvest*?**
   A. the growing of rice and grains
   B. the bringing in of crops
   C. the selling of rice to buyers
   D. the celebration of a food crop

2. **In which state is the Crowley International Rice Festival held?**
   A. New York   C. Louisiana
   B. California   D. Nevada

3. **Which is NOT a way the people of Crowley celebrate the natural resource of rice?**
   A. They give away free rice in the stores.
   B. They use rice in cooking contests
   C. They decorate lampposts and floats with rice.
   D. They eat foods made with rice.

4. **Why is rice so important to the people of Crowley?**
   A. Rice helps many people there earn a living.
   B. The people of Crowley like the way rice tastes.
   C. It is the only crop that grows in Crowley.
   D. People in Crowley like to have rice cooking contests.

5. **A *Cajun* is someone whose family comes from —**
   A. Italian settlers who came to California to grow grapes for wine
   B. Canadian people who moved to New York in the 1800s
   C. British settlers who first came to America in the 1700s
   D. French-speaking people who moved to Louisiana in the 1700s

Name _____ Date _____

Environment and Society

How Did Swedish Settlers Build Their New Lives?

Many Swedish settlers moved to Minnesota. The land and climate reminded them of Sweden. Use the map below to answer the questions.

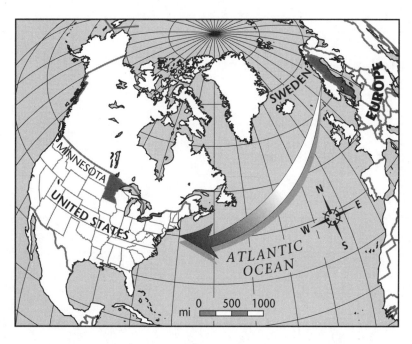

1. **Which ocean did Swedish settlers cross to reach the United States?**

    _____

2. **Which is farther north, Sweden or Minnesota? How can you tell?**

    _____

3. **Place an X on the map to show where you live. Would the climate in your region make Swedish visitors feel "at home"? Tell why or why not.**

    _____

Name _____ Date _____

Locating Vietnam

Label the continents shown here. Color in the country of Vietnam. Use pages 230–231 in your book to help you. Use the map below to answer these questions.

1. Which continent to the south is closest to Vietnam?

_____

2. China is located on which continent?

_____

3. Which ocean is east of Vietnam?

_____

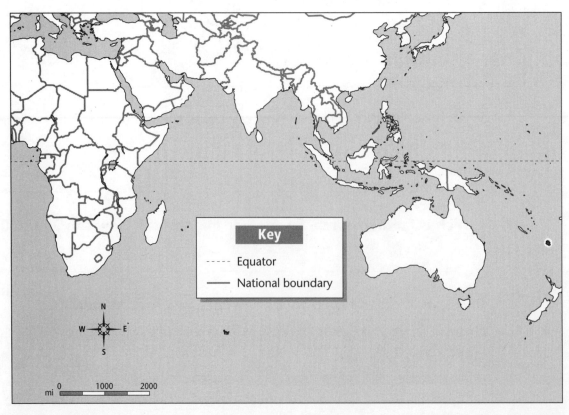

Key

- - - - Equator

———— National boundary

Name _____ Date _____

Our Country Celebrates

Review pages 232–245 to answer these questions. Choose the best
answer. Circle the letter next to your choice.

1. **What is a *fossil*?**
   A. the remains of a plant or animal from long ago
   B. another name for a fireworks show
   C. a life-size model of a dinosaur
   D. a museum in Rapid City, South Dakota

2. **The Independence Day celebration in Washington, D.C., ends
   with a —**
   A. parade
   B. fireworks display
   C. concert
   D. reading of the Declaration of Independence

3. **What do all Fourth of July celebrations have in common?**
   A. They all have hot dogs and watermelon.
   B. They have fireworks displays at night.
   C. They celebrate pride in the United States.
   D. They remind us of the history of our local communities.

4. **The Declaration of Independence is a document that —**
   A. tells people how they might celebrate the Fourth of July
   B. explains reasons the 13 colonies in America wanted to be free
   C. shares people's language, customs, and beliefs
   D. states the laws of the United States

5. **An example of Cajun cooking is —**
   A. spaghetti   C. boudin
   B. hamburgers   D. pizza

Name _____ Date _____

6. **Which instruments are often used to play Cajun music?**

    A. flutes and clarinets

    B. accordions and fiddles

    C. drums and cymbals

    D. trumpets and trombones

7. **The Crowley International Rice Festival is like —**

    A. Christmas, because they both take place in December

    B. a birthday party, because people bring gifts

    C. the Fourth of July, because both are celebrated everywhere

    D. Thanksgiving, because both celebrate food crops

8. **What is special about community festivals?**

    A. They give people in the community a day off from work.

    B. They help people find something to do with their time.

    C. They bring people together to have fun and celebrate their
       heritage.

    D. They give children in the community a chance to be in a
       parade.

9. **In which state do many Cajuns live?**

    A. California

    B. Pennsylvania

    C. North Dakota

    D. Louisiana

10. **Which of the following people in Crowley do NOT use rice in
    their jobs?**

    A. police

    B. farmers

    C. restaurant cooks

    D. supermarket workers

Name _____ Date _____

Comprehension Skill: Topic, Main Idea, and Supporting Details

Celebrating Cultures

A **topic** is the subject of a piece of writing. **Main ideas** are the most important ideas stated about the topic. **Supporting details** give more information about the main ideas.

1. **Here is the topic, main idea, and one supporting detail from page 254 of Lesson 1. Write another supporting detail in the empty box.**

Topic: The Many Cultures of Ghana

Main Idea

Ghana has a great deal of cultural diversity

Supporting Detail	Supporting Detail
The people of Ghana belong to as many as 100 different ethnic groups.	

2–4. **Now read pages 255–256. Fill in the chart below. Write one main idea and two supporting details.**

Topic: A Harvest Festival in Ghana

Main Idea

Supporting Detail	Supporting Detail

Name _____ Date _____

Celebrating Cultures

Review pages 253–257 to answer these questions. Choose the best answer. Circle the letter next to your choice.

1. **On which continent is Ghana located?**
   A. Asia
   B. Africa
   C. Europe
   D. South America

2. **Ghana's tropical climate means that the country is —**
   A. cold and wet
   B. windy and cool
   C. hot and humid
   D. very hot and dry

3. **The many different ethnic groups in Ghana create a great deal of —**
   A. trade
   B. territory
   C. air pollution
   D. cultural diversity

4. **Which of the following do people do during Homowo?**
   A. stay inside
   B. eat nothing
   C. fish for lobster
   D. settle misunderstandings

5. **The cloth the Ashanti weave is called —**
   A. kente
   B. kpoikpoi
   C. technology
   D. transportation

Lesson Review

Name _____ Date _____

Using Latitude and Longitude

Finding Places with Numbers

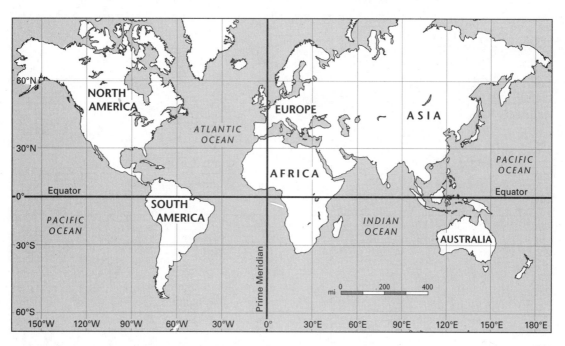

Use the map above to answer the following questions.

1. **Through which oceans does the equator run?**

   _____

2. **Through which continents does the prime meridian run?**

   _____

3. **Which continent is completely north of the equator and west of the prime meridian?**

   _____

4. **Which continent is completely south of the equator and east of the prime meridian?**

   _____

Name _____ Date _____

Using Latitude and Longitude

X Marks the Spot

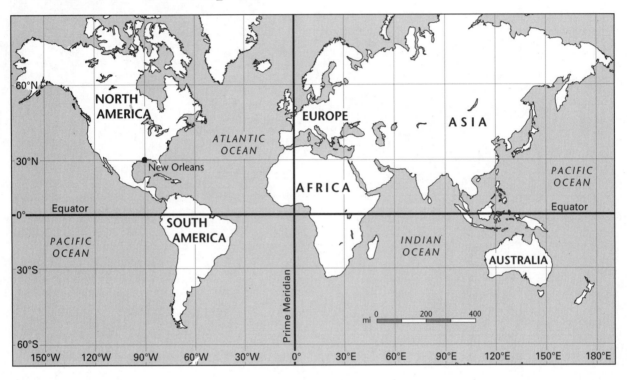

Use the map above to answer the following questions.

1. **Name the lines of latitude that pass through Asia.**

   _____

2. **Name the lines of longitude that pass through Australia.**

   _____

3. **If you are at 30°S and 60°W, on which continent are you?**

   _____

4. **If you are at 0° latitude and 60°E, in which ocean are you?**

   _____

Skills Workshop

Name _____ Date _____

Comprehension Skill: Making Predictions

Celebrating a New Year

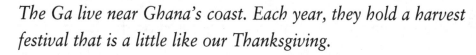

A **prediction** is a thoughtful guess about the future. To make a prediction when you are reading, think about what has happened so far in the book. Also think about what you know in real life.

1. **The passage below is based on information on page 255. Read it, then circle the most likely prediction.**

    The Ga live near Ghana's coast. Each year, they hold a harvest festival that is a little like our Thanksgiving.

    A. Dancing will be part of the festival.
    B. Food will be part of the festival.
    C. This festival will honor sports heroes.

2. **Read "Preparing for a New Year" on page 265 and "Days of Celebration" on pages 266–267. Suppose it is January 10th— two weeks before the lunar New Year. You are going to Vietnam. Circle two predictions about what you will see.**

    A. I will see a celebration of the harvest.
    B. I will see many red decorations on homes.
    C. I will see special foods in the stores.

3. **Imagine going to a New Year's Eve celebration in Vietnam. What might you see or hear at midnight or the next day?**

    _____

    _____

Name _____ Date _____

Celebrating a New Year

Review pages 264–267 to answer these questions. Choose the best answer. Circle the letter next to your choice.

1. **Where is Vietnam?**
   A. in Southeast Asia   C. in South America
   B. in Eastern Europe   D. in West Africa

2. **What does *lunar* mean?**
   A. having to do with space   C. returning of spring
   B. beginning a new year   D. based on the moon

3. **Which is NOT a way people prepare for the New Year in Vietnam?**
   A. by cleaning and decorating their homes, temples, and churches
   B. by buying new clothes and gifts to wear at special celebrations
   C. by placing coins and flowers in shoes outside their homes
   D. by preparing special foods for their friends and family members

4. **What is an *altar*?**
   A. a popular beach where tourists like to visit in Vietnam
   B. a table or raised place that is used during religious services
   C. a tower in a church where people go for special times of worship
   D. a special food prepared by the Vietnamese on New Year's Day

5. **What is an *ancestor*?**
   A. someone you remember from long ago
   B. a picture of a very good friend
   C. a relative who has died
   D. a piece of wood with someone's name on it

Name _____ Date _____

A World of Celebrations

Review pages 253–267 to answer these questions. Choose the best answer. Circle the letter next to your choice.

1. **Which of the following do the people of Ghana share?**
   A. one food
   B. one culture
   C. one type of transportation
   D. one president and government

2. **To make certain people in Ghana can understand each other at work, they often speak —**
   A. English   C. Spanish
   B. French   D. Japanese

3. **Which of the following is one way people celebrate Homowo?**
   A. They paint their houses.
   B. They sell their old clothes.
   C. They buy seeds and plant their gardens.
   D. They dress up in colorful clothes and make lots of noise.

4. **The mixture of corn meal and palm oil eaten at Homowo is called —**
   A. bai vi   C. tradition
   B. kpoikpoi   D. agriculture

5. **Which of the following describes kente cloth?**
   A. dull looking
   B. made from leather
   C. all black and very rough
   D. bold patterns and bright colors

Name _____ Date _____

6. **What special food is eaten during the Vietnamese New Year's celebration?**
   A. strawberry jelly
   B. sweet rice cakes
   C. corn on the cob
   D. chocolate cupcakes

7. **What is another name for the New Year's holiday in Vietnam?**
   A. Tet
   B. Red Day
   C. Carnival
   D. Happy Day

8. **What does the color red mean to people in Vietnam?**
   A. money
   B. happiness
   C. good health
   D. remembering the past

9. **People build altars during the New Year's festival to —**
   A. bring good luck
   B. bring happy dreams
   C. honor their ancestors
   D. keep away unfriendly visitors

10. **On the first morning of the New Year, families give children —**
    A. new toys and clothes
    B. baskets of candy and cookies
    C. gifts of money in red envelopes
    D. rules to follow during the new year

Name _____ Date _____

Comprehension Strategy: Previewing a Lesson

Our Local Governments

You have learned that when you **preview** a lesson, you look ahead at it. To preview Lesson 1, follow these steps.

Write the title and Main Idea of Lesson 1 from page 275 here.

1. Title: _____

2. Main Idea: _____

_____

Read the other headings and Focus questions. Write the headings here.

3. page 276: _____

4. page 278: _____

Now look at the pictures in Lesson 1. What kinds of community members do you see in the pictures on these pages? Write your answers below.

5. page 275: _____

6. page 276: _____

7. page 277: _____

8. page 279: _____

9. Think about the headings, Focus questions, and pictures. What do you think you will learn in Lesson 1?

_____

_____

Name _____ Date _____

Our Local Governments

Review pages 275–279 to answer these questions. Choose the best answer. Circle the letter next to your choice.

1. **What services do local governments provide?**
   A. special laws about things like seat belts
   B. neighborhood parks, libraries, and recycling
   C. laws that the whole country must follow
   D. new roads, state hospitals, and water resources

2. **What is a *citizen*?**
   A. an official member of a country, state, or community
   B. a person who belongs to a special groups of leaders
   C. an area within a state that has its own government
   D. someone who wants to be elected to do a special job

3. **What is one thing people must do to become citizens?**
   A. They must swear loyalty to the country they came from.
   B. They must live in the U.S. for several years.
   C. They must only have been born in the United States.
   D. They must pay a large sum of money to the President.

4. **What is a *public place*?**
   A. a place that belongs to only one person
   B. a place that belongs to one group of people
   C. a place that you must have permission to use
   D. a place that can be used by everyone

5. **What is a *private place*?**
   A. a place like a library or community park
   B. a place that you can go to anytime
   C. a place that you must have permission to use
   D. a place that can be used by everyone

Lesson Review

Name _____ Date _____

Vocabulary Skill: Words About a Topic

Our County Governments

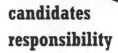

Lesson 2 is about how county governments work.
Here are some of the words used to talk about government.

records	parishes	elected	candidates
citizens	boroughs	voting	responsibility

Write each word under the sentence that tells about it. If you need help,
find the word on page 283 of Lesson 2 and read how it is used.

1. **This word names people who run for a government job.**

   _____

2. **This process gives people the right to choose their leaders.**

   _____

3-4. **These are two words for "counties."**

   _____

5. **These hold written information so people will remember it.**

   _____

6. **This word names members of a country.**

   _____

7. **This means "chosen by voting."**

   _____

8. **This is another word for "duty."**

   _____

Name _____ Date _____

Our County Governments

Review pages 282–285 to answer these questions. Choose the best
answer. Circle the letter next to your choice.

1. **What is a *county*?**
   A. a community just outside of a city
   B. land that is an official part of another country
   C. part of a state that has its own government
   D. a rule that people must follow to keep order

2. **What might you see at county fairgrounds?**
   A. lots of books that you can borrow
   B. many people in bathing suits
   C. old dinosaur bones and tools used to find them
   D. flowers, vegetables, and animals

3. **Which is a NOT a job of county governments?**
   A. helping to give police protection
   B. helping to build new shopping malls
   C. helping to give children public schools
   D. helping to build airports

4. **What is a *candidate*?**
   A. a winner at the county fair
   B. a person voting for the first time
   C. someone running for a government job
   D. an area set aside for voting

5. **It is a voter's right to —**
   A. vote when he or she turns 16
   B. help choose the best leaders
   C. learn about farming at a county fair
   D. vote anywhere he or she likes

Name _____ Date _____

Environment and Society

How Do People Change the Environment?

Use the map above to answer the following questions.

1. **Which two states border the Chesapeake Bay?**

   _____

2. **Name two rivers that flow into the Chesapeake Bay.**

   _____

3. **A family lives along the Wicomico River. They spray a
   chemical on their lawn. They also wash their dog and then
   dump the soapy water into the river. How might their actions
   change the Chesapeake Bay?** _____

   _____

Think Like a Geographer   Workbook for Reading and Review   **109**

Name _____ Date _____

States and Capitals

1. Write a number from 1–10 in any 10 states.

2. Use another sheet of paper to write the name of the capital city next to each number.

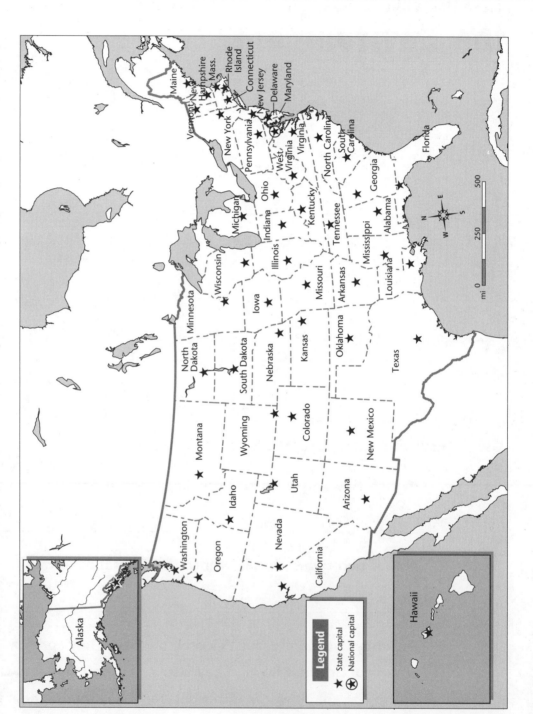

Name _____ Date _____

Comprehension Skill: Understanding Text Organization–Special Features

Our State Governments

Your textbook has many **special features.** Special features give more information about the topic of the lesson. You often find them at the bottom or the sides of the pages in your book.

1. **Read the "Tell Me More" special feature on page 289. What information does it give? Answer with a complete sentence.**

   _____

2. **Why does the "Tell Me More" feature belong in a lesson about state government?**

   _____

   _____

3. **Now look at the special feature on page 290. What does it show?**

   _____

4. **What information about state government does it give?**

   _____

   _____

5. **Three small maps of the United States appear in Lesson 3. What pages are the maps on?**

   _____

6. **What information do these maps give?**

   _____

Name _____ Date _____

Our State Governments

Review pages 288–292 to answer these questions. Choose the best answer. Circle the letter next to your choice.

1. What is a *border*?

    A. the line where one state ends and another begins

    B. a restaurant where foods from one state are served

    C. a special law of each state

    D. another name for a state police officer

2. Which is NOT a difference between states?

    A. different state flags

    B. different speed laws

    C. different Presidents

    D. different state flowers

3. What does state government do?

    A. meets in Washington, D.C., each month

    B. makes laws, helps people, and collects tax money

    C. provides county fairs to help people have fun

    D. builds new businesses and makes new products

4. What is a *governor*?

    A. the person chosen by voters to be the head of state government

    B. a person who must pay state taxes

    C. someone who goes to school to teach students about safety

    D. the organization that keeps the state in order

5. What is the *legislature*?

    A. all the laws of a state that the people must obey

    B. a law that says that citizens of a state should vote

    C. money raised by the state to pay for state programs

    D. the group of people who make state laws

Name _____ Date _____

Study Skill: Taking Notes

Our National Government

When you **take notes** you write down words or
phrases that sum up main ideas and details from
your textbook. When you read your notes later, they remind you
of what you read. Here are some notes for page 294.

> **Page 294: National government**
> - makes decisions and passes laws, has three branches
> - President is leader of the country and head of the first branch
> - Congress is second branch
> - Congress makes laws, members chosen by voters

Now try taking notes yourself. Read Lesson 4. Stop after reading each
page and write notes that sum up the information. You don't have to
write complete sentences.

1. Page 295

_____

_____

2. Governments Work Together (page 296)

_____

_____

3. Rights and Responsibilities (page 297)

_____

_____

Name _____ Date _____

Our National Government

Review pages 293–297 to answer these questions. Choose the best answer. Circle the letter next to your choice.

1. **What happens in Washington, D.C., in January?**

   A. People vote for a new President.

   B. People move in to begin new jobs in government.

   C. People visit important buildings there.

   D. People fly here because airplane tickets are cheap.

2. **What is the *President*?**

   A. the leader of the government of Great Britain

   B. a judge on the Supreme Court

   C. the person who makes laws for the state government

   D. the head of the government of the United States

3. **Where does the President live?**

   A. the White House   C. the Congress

   B. the Capitol   D. the Constitution

4. **What is the *Congress*?**

   A. the leader of the United States government

   B. the name of the street where the President lives

   C. people who meet to make laws for the United States

   D. a place where people answer questions about the law

5. **How is Congress chosen?**

   A. The President chooses members of Congress.

   B. Voters elect members of Congress.

   C. Congress is chosen by the judges on the Supreme Court.

   D. Members of Congress from the year before choose new members of Congress.

Name _____ Date _____

Comparing Tables and Graphs
How Much? How Many?

Study this table and graph and find out about the
populations of Florida and Michigan.

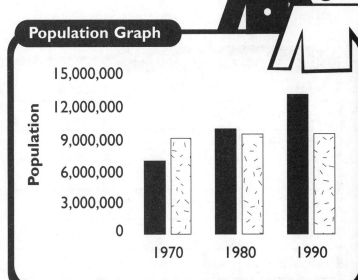

Population Table		
	Florida	**Michigan**
1970	6,791,418	8,881,826
1980	9,746,961	9,262,044
1990	12,937,926	9,295,297

Population Graph

1. **Look at the table. Which state had the larger population in 1970? What was its population?**

   _____

2. **Look at the graph. Which state grew more from 1970 to 1980?**

   _____

3. **Between 1980 and 1990, Michigan's population grew. Which tells this fact better, the chart or the graph? Why?**

   _____

   _____

   _____

Name _____ Date _____

Comparing Tables and Graphs

Animals All Around

Some children in Kansas started a table and graph to show
what animals they raised. Help them finish it. Read the graph
and table. Then answer the questions.

Table of Farm Animals		
Name	**1997**	**1998**
John	pig	pig
Gina	goat	goat
Lisa	goat	chicken
Alan	chicken	goat
James	chicken	chicken
Danielle		
Travis		

Graph: Animals raised in 1997

5

4

3

2 □ □

1 □ □ □

pigs   goats   chickens

1. **Add this information to the table:**
   Danielle raised a goat in 1997 and a pig in 1998.
   Travis raised one pig in 1997 and another pig in 1998.

2. **Use the 1997 information you added to the table to complete
   the graph.**

3. **To find the animal more children raised in 1997, is it quicker to
   read the table or the graph?**

   _____

4. **Add the 1998 information to the graph. Draw the bars right
   next to the ones for 1997. Label the bars 1997 and 1998.
   Remember to change the title of the graph.**

Skills Workshop

Name _____ Date _____

Government in the United States

Review pages 274–297 to answer these questions. Choose the best answer. Circle the letter next to your choice.

1. **What do taxes pay for?**
    A. shopping malls, grocery stores, and parking lots
    B. firefighting, public libraries, parks, and schools
    C. clothing, food, water, gas, and electricity
    D. office buildings, private parks, and advertising

2. **How do communities pay for public places?**
    A. with lotteries
    B. with local taxes
    C. with entrance fees
    D. with bake sales

3. **Who started the first library in 1731?**
    A. King William
    B. George Washington
    C. Benjamin Franklin
    D. William Henry Jackson

4. **How does county government help people?**
    A. Counties make laws for the whole state.
    B. Counties keep records of births and voters.
    C. Counties help the governments of other states.
    D. Counties provide new restaurants and movie theaters.

5. **The head of state government is called a —**
    A. senator
    B. President
    C. mayor
    D. governor

Name _____   Date _____

6. **Where is our national government located?**

   A. Washington, D.C.   C. Los Angeles, California

   B. New York City   D. Miami, Florida

7. **What is the highest court in the United States?**

   A. the Supreme Court

   B. the word of the President

   C. the United Nations

   D. UNICEF

8. **Which is an example of how different levels of government work together?**

   A. State governments work to provide clean, safe state parks.

   B. National government tells how money should be spent by the state government.

   C. National and state governments work together to build safe highways.

   D. Local government provides campaigns to begin recycling programs in schools.

9. **What is the *Constitution*?**

   A. a branch of the government that makes all the laws of the country

   B. the head of a branch of the national government

   C. the basic laws and ideas that the U.S. government follows

   D. the name of the building where the national government meets

10. **The Bill of Rights —**

   A. tells citizens how to vote

   B. tells citizens of their rights and responsibilities

   C. is the cost of running the government each year

   D. says that different levels of government must work together

Name _____ Date _____

Study Skill: Making an Outline

Looking at Governments

Remember that an **outline** is a set of organized notes. In an outline, **main topics** are written next to Roman numerals (I, II, III). Important **details** are written next to capital letters (A, B, C). Here is an outline of the information on page 309:

    I. Looking at Governments

        A. The United States Congress is made up of 535 lawmakers.

        B. 150 lawmakers rule the Netherlands.

        C. Governments around the world create laws.

Now try filling in the next part of the outline. Write the heading on page 310 next to Roman numeral II. Write details next to the capital letters.

    II. _____

        A. _____

        B. _____

Now finish the outline for Lesson 1. The headings have been filled in for you.

    III. What Governments Do (pages 312–313)

        A. _____

        B. _____

    IV. National Governments (pages 314–315)

        A. _____

        B. _____

        C. _____

Name _____ Date _____

Looking at Governments

Review pages 309–315 to answer these questions. Choose the best
answer. Circle the letter next to your choice.

1. **In what way is the government of the Netherlands like the
    government of the United States?**

    A. Both governments are headed by a President elected by the
       people.

    B. Both governments have a branch that makes laws.

    C. All lawmakers in both countries are elected to represent the
       whole country.

    D. Both governments have a queen.

2. **In which continent is the Netherlands?**

    A. Australia   C. North America

    B. Asia   D. Europe

3. **Which group in the Netherlands makes laws?**

    A. the House of Representatives

    B. the Congress

    C. the parliament

    D. the court

4. **How do citizens in the Netherlands choose lawmakers?**

    A. by voting only once every two years

    B. by voting for lawmakers that represent the whole country

    C. by only voting for lawmakers that live in their area

    D. by voting for a queen every four years

5. **Which job in the Netherlands is like the job of the President
    of the United States?**

    A. the prime minister   C. the governor

    B. the queen   D. the general

Name _____ Date _____

Using the Media
What's New?

Newspapers, radio, magazines, television, and the Internet are kinds of media. They give us different kinds of information. For example, in a magazine, you might read this about nine-year-old Courtney Renner, a young ice skater with big hopes:

Ice Cool

At 7 A.M., when most kids are just crawling out of bed, Courtney Renner is jumping on the ice. Courtney, who lives in Crofton, Maryland, is a figure skater. She hopes to skate in the Olympics someday. To get ready, Courtney practices for three hours every morning.

Write the name of one kind of media (newspaper, radio, magazine, television, Internet) that you might use to do the following.

1. **Watch a favorite skater in action.** _____

2. **Read an article about how Courtney Renner trains for the**

   Olympics. _____

3. **Use a computer to "chat" with other kids who are skating fans.**

   _____

4. **Listen to a sports report telling how the skaters did in**

   competitions. _____

Name _____ Date _____

Using the Media
Reporting Current Events

You know that different media can give you different kinds of information about a subject. Choose a sports star or performer who is in the news. Then choose two kinds of media to find out about him or her.

1. **My subject** (person):

   _____

2. **Something I would like to know:**

   _____

   _____

   _____

3. **Media I would use** (check two):
   - ☐ radio
   - ☐ television
   - ☐ Internet
   - ☐ newspaper
   - ☐ magazine

4. **Why I think both kinds of media would give the information I want:**

   _____

   _____

   _____

Name _____ Date _____

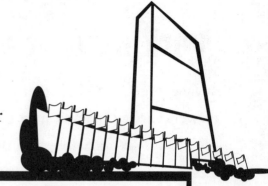

Comprehension Skill: Summarizing Long Passages

Working Across Borders

When you **summarize,** you retell important ideas in your own words. Here is a summary of page 319.

> *Governments work together in many ways. Most nations are part of the United Nations. Ambassadors try to make life better for people around the world. UNICEF works to help the world's children.*

Read pages 320–323. Write the main ideas on the lines below.

Page 320

1. **What is one other reason governments work together?**

_____

Page 321

2. **What did the United States and Russia begin to do in 1994?**

_____

Page 322

3. **What event brings people from around the world together?**

_____

Page 323

4. **What are exchange programs?** _____

5. **Why are they important?** _____

6. **Now write a summary of pages 320–323 on another sheet of paper. Include the main ideas above in your summary.**

Name _____ Date _____

Working Across Borders

Review pages 318–323 to answer these questions. Choose the best answer. Circle the letter next to your choice.

1. Who belongs to the United Nations?

   A. people who want to help animals and save the environment

   B. ambassadors from almost every nation to help governments work together

   C. men and women who are elected by their citizens to make the world peaceful

   D. persons from every state in the United States to make our world a better place

2. Where does the United Nations meet?

   A. Washington, D.C.   C. the Netherlands

   B. in different cities   D. New York City

3. UNICEF is —

   A. a part of the United Nations that helps children around the world

   B. an organization that helps scientists from around the world work together

   C. a group that sends athletes to train in different countries

   D. Uniting Nations In Consideration of Every Family

4. Which did Andrew Young NOT do?

   A. work with Dr. Martin Luther King, Jr.

   B. run for President of the United States

   C. serve as mayor of Atlanta, Georgia

   D. head the Olympics organizing committee

5. What does *ban* mean?

   A. to run for office   C. to kill a whale

   B. to win a sporting event   D. to forbid by law

Name _____ Date _____

Our Nation and the World

Review pages 308–323 to answer these questions. Choose the best answer. Circle the letter next to your choice.

1. **How does the Queen of the Netherlands help her government?**

    A. by giving the government ideas on how to solve problems

    B. by meeting with lawmakers and approving the laws they make

    C. by being in charge of the courts in her country

    D. by deciding how the country's money will be spent

2. **Another name for the Netherlands is —**

    A. Dutchland   C. Holland

    B. Tulipland   D. North Province

3. **What is a *dike*?**

    A. a landing place where ships tie up to load and unload cargo

    B. fine dirt particles that floodwater carries

    C. a wide highway built to help traffic move quickly

    D. mounded earth that keeps water out of new land

4. **What is the job of Water Control Boards in the Netherlands?**

    A. to keep land from flooding

    B. to stop water pollution

    C. to be sure there is enough drinking water

    D. to keep people safe while boating and swimming

5. **An ambassador is a person who —**

    A. wants to be elected to a government job

    B. serves as a representative from the government of another country

    C. serves as the head of a state's government

    D. translates from one language into another

Name _____ Date _____

6. **What does a *translator* do?**

   A. listens to what someone says in one language and repeats it in another language

   B. writes down everything that another person says so others can have a copy of it

   C. listens to the words of another person and writes it in a story for the newspaper

   D. reports what someone has said in a radio speech

7. **How did Russians and Americans work together?**

   A. They joined UNICEF to help hungry Russian children.

   B. They lived and worked together on a space station.

   C. They helped each other's countries save money by providing cheap airfares.

   D. They went to the Olympics in Greece to help people get along.

8. **Which organization brings together athletes from all over the world?**

   A. UNICEF   C. the Olympics

   B. the United Nations   D. Russian Cosmonauts

9. **Which organization helps girls all over the world get to know one another?**

   A. the World Organization for Girls from All Nations

   B. the World Association of Girl Guides and Girl Scouts

   C. the United Nations

   D. the Olympics for Girls

10. **An *exchange program* is a program in which —**

    A. athletes train in each other's countries

    B. singers visit other countries to learn about music

    C. countries exchange ideas about government

    D. students live and study in another country